"Hey, Taxi!"

"Hey, Taxi!"

Tales Told in Taxies
and Recounted by Cabbies

by

Hanoch Teller

New York City Publishing Company

ISBN 0-9614772-8-8

Library of Congress Registration Number TX 3 080 284

1 5   1 4   1 3   1 2   1 1   1 0   9   8   7

Distributed by
FELDHEIM PUBLISHERS
200 Airport Executive Park
Nanuet, NY 10954
FELDHEIM PUBLISHERS
POB 35002, Jerusalem, ISRAEL

J. LEHMANN
Hebrew Booksellers
20 Cambridge Terrace
Gateshead
Tyne & Wear

*The Jewish tradition
of the Story:*

*It can bring people back to a
certain time;
And it can bring people back
to where they belong.
It is a tradition which safeguards
Tradition.*

In tribute to our children לאי"ט

Chaim Baruch and **Etti**   **Reuven Yehoshua**
Sara Faigel, Moredechai Shimon,
Rivka, Shifra, and Yehuda

לעילוי נשמת
In Loving Memory of

Zalman Aaron Chibowski z"l
זלמן אהרון צ'יבוסקי ז"ל

10th of Nissan 5734
י' ניסן תשל"ד

A quiet and humble man who rebuilt a life,
a family, and a legacy after surviving the ashes of
Europe. In the New World where temptations
abounded, his Shabbos observance was never up
for negotiation, nor were the principles of
Judaism.

Zalman Aaron did what he had to do, because it
had to get done — never for ulterior motivations.
Every shul and every organization in the Bronx
wished to honor him at their dinner, but receiving
recognition was as foreign to this modest man as
was the possibility that he would ever refuse to
offer assistance. His hand was open to everyone,
and all he ever asked in return was that his
donations be kept anonymous.

His desire to settle in the land of Israel remained
but a dream. At a young age — but after a life
filled with accomplishment — he merited only to
be buried in the Holy Land.

ת.נ.צ.ב.ה.

Also by
Hanoch Teller

APPROBATION FROM HAGAON HARAV REPHAEL SHMUELEVITZ Shlita

ב"ה תשרי תשנ"א

כבוד ידידי החשוב, ידיו רב לו
בקירוב הבריות לאביהם שבשמים
הרב' ר' חנוך טלר שליט"א

שלום רב לאוהבי תורתיך

שמחתי לשמוע על הופעת ספר נוסף מסדרת ספריך
העוסקת בסיפורים הלקוחים מן החיים, המעוררים לב
הבריות לקרבם לאמונה ולבטחון ולטוהר המדות --
אשר הנה באמת עבודת כל האדם -- שרבות שמעתי בדבר
השפעתם הברוכה על הצבור הרחב של דוברי אנגלית
בארץ ישראל ובחו"ל, לעורר לב בנים אל אביהם
שבשמים.

ואכן שמעתי מאמאמו"ר זצ"ל בשם הגה"צ ר' ירוחם
זצ"ל שבעניני הבטחון בה' אין דרך ההשפעה ע"י
דברי חכמה עמוקים, אלא ע"י דברים פשוטים המדברים
אל לב כל אדם, וע"י דוגמאות מעשיות מהחיים
המביאים לידי אמונה פשוטה, ואכן ספריך מלאים
ודגושים בכגון זאת, ואף בשאר עניני עבודת ה'
וטוהר המדות יש השפעה רבה להמחשת הדברים ע"י
תיאורים חיים הלקוחים מן המציאות.

ע"כ אמרתי לבוא במכתב זה לחזק ידיד ידיד בעבודת הקודש
הזו, אשר היא משתלבת עם עבודתך הברוכה, רבות
הפירות, בהרצאות וטייעפים בקרב קהילות ישראל
בחו"ל. ולברך אותך שתמשיך בעבודת הקודש שלקחת
על עצמך, ועוד למצוא אפיקים נוספים של זיכוי
הרבים וקירובם לתורה וליראת שמים כיד ה' הטובה
עליך.

שוכן מרומים יברכך בכל מילי דמיטב

בס"ד

כבר אמרתי שברכה להם הוא הרה"ג ר' יעקב שי'

שליט"א, אור ברכה וטובה את החכם כספרי מעלי

כיקרים וכלו תורה ונספרי אמות זוכות ויו"ו

האמת וירות שמים, את כל עצה יפה עליו, ואין

לאיר עוד התעלות השמים מספרו לחכם כהם

כראוי.

אך כן יום כשורה הוא לי שאעשנו היום זאת

אושר כס"ד להוליא לאור דוד ספר. ולהוסיף לאמת

לספרין אך לאמיתו הוא, כי כפו סאנ" כקט עשה

ונתת ואמתקום שלמים של ראשון, אבל ידע כי יבוא

את נותת עלן לו כשאות את ברכתי כי הם

כאות ולהם כאו יובן מעישותו חולה, כן ירבה

וכן יפרו, עד אשר האמ דעת דעה, ומלאה

הכתיבה לשונה יברא האחבר לשונה ותמלא

ובכה עד כי בית ירון, לקבל פן מלית

ברכת מאהבה דלו,

נאמנות אנכם ואמקירו,

צעיר הלוים

אביגדר נבנצל

Contents

ב"ה

Acknowledgments and Disclaimer

DEAREST READER,

Half a decade ago, we embarked together on a bold literary experiment to determine the feasibility of conveying vital Torah lessons through literature that is contemporary in style yet ancient in approach. This type of literature has come to be known as "soul stories," inspiring tales of ordinary people who do extraordinary things, modern spiritual heroes and heroines who touch the soul of the readers and strike a responsive chord in their heart.

Apparently the Almighty favored the venture, and people from every part of the globe and every walk of life have written and phoned me to relate similarly inspiring tales of their own. Those stories formed the kernel for several "soulful" volumes.

Then, after a brief literary detour (three titles long), I returned with *Pichifkes* to where I began — recounting stories I'd heard on the road. And now, once again, having sorted, sifted, and ultimately compiled this present anthology, I thank Providence for the privilege of offering "Hey, Taxi!" — inspirational stories heard by the "traveling man" that I have become.

For better or worse, my name is often identified with this old-new literary genre, due, perhaps, to a quirk of fate. Like the medical columnist named Dr. Nourse or the electrician Mr. Shocken, it is possible that my profession chose me, instead of the other way around. It is, therefore, with conflicting emotions that I offer this, my final volume of soul stories.

Final? you may ask. My faithful readers might contend that the longish short story, projecting the truth as it exists in the soul of one writer, has so affected Jewish hearts and minds that it must be allowed to continue flourishing. While I would welcome and appreciate such a vote of confidence, I maintain that it is the story itself that is immutable, not its writer.

An author is obliged to change — both in response to and in anticipation of the changes that visit the lives of his readers. Contemporary prose is both a reflection and a definer of its times. Show me prose that doesn't change with change, and I'll show you prose perfect for wrapping fish.

Several Introductions ago, reference was made to the author who would gladly exchange one hundred readers today for one reader one hundred years from now. Such an achievement would tell us a great deal about the author's skill: that he influenced the thought and deed of men; that he helped to alter the course of writing; that he produced a work of art; or that he so brilliantly captured a time, place or figure that to go back and reread his work would pay historical, as well as literary, dividends. If an author has failed to accomplish any of the above, his composition is as meaningful as outdated phone books.

Our Sages have added one additional, invaluable criterion for making a modest impact: דברים היוצאים מן הלב נכנסים אל הלב — "Words that emanate from the heart, penetrate the heart." Oratory and literature — no matter how eloquent or creative — which do not meet this last condition will not withstand the test of time.

I doubt that any of my humble scribblings will qualify as a classic to be reread a hundred years hence. Still, I retain the hope that my contemporary readers will occasionally re-examine, or at least remember, the essential, timeless lessons these stories are intended to convey. They do, indeed, emanate from my heart.

There is something particularly enchanting about taxi drivers, the supporting characters of this book. None, or certainly few of them, admit to their chosen profession. Each one claims he is only "doing this" part-time, and that he is *really*: (an actor) (a prize fighter) (a writer) (a beautician).

Choose one or all of the above. One time — it was in Antwerp — I met a genuine, full-time cab driver with no pipe dream of a better future.

All of those friends I would like to acknowledge and thank for their help are employed full time at other pursuits, although from their unstinting response to my sometimes outrageous requests, one would never know it. They are indeed *my* supporting characters, in the most literal sense.

First and foremost, I extend my gratitude to the remarkably talented Yechiel Kapiloff and remarkably gracious Rebbetzin Rookie Billet. Leibel Estrin and Chaim Meirson have been my partners in creation for several books running, as has been an anonymous friend and mentor, endeavor after endeavor. My steadfast typist, Dubba Raizel Figus, has redefined the expression "above and beyond the call of duty."

While I was in America this past summer, Les Schachter, Al Hirsch, and Dr. Heshy Jacobs were eager to lend their gifted hands (or computers, respectively) to this project, and I am indebted to them equally.

Completing the production of a book, or, as it's known colloquially, "making it happen," at the record-breaking speed of "*Hey, Taxi!*" required the teamwork and devotion of New York City Publishing Company, the drive of Baruch Baruchman, the gracious cooperation of Feldheim Publishers, the graphic talents of S. Binyomin Ginsberg, and the unrivaled literary genius of Marsi Tabak.

No Author doth his Novelle make,

Nor doth Redactor quill uptake;

No Printer's thirst for gold be slak'd,

Nor Binder from his Slumber wake;

'Til suns o'er far Horizons break,

And friends be Friends for friendship's Sake.

I would hope the anonymous, though presumably famous, author of the paraphrased sextet above will forgive my mangling of it to make a point. I have never deluded myself into believing that any single participant in the book production process could possibly produce a book without the contributions of all the others.

Rabbi Yonason David once told me that if I wish to improve as a teacher, I should study more Torah. What he meant — or certainly what I understood — was that the more Torah a person knows, the better he will be at any endeavor. Expertise in a given area is achieved through the accumulation of teachings and experiences in a host of different areas.

I therefore wish to arise and proclaim my gratitude to all those who have helped and directed me, from my *Rosh Yeshivah* under whom I have learned for over a dozen years, to a student who has clarified an exegetic profundity. More chronologically, my gratitude begins with my beloved parents, about whom someone once insightfully remarked: "The Tellers are more than a family; they're a team!" For a decade-and-a-half, Rabbi Yitzchok and Rebbetzin Bernice Ginsberg have also been like family.

To the young and aspiring who will need friendship and guidance, I wish the good fortune that I encountered in stumbling upon the Benjie Brechers, Ronnie Rosenbergs, Yitzchok Rosenbergs, Joseph Telushkins, and Mordche Weinstocks of this world.

To SHALOM and SHAINDY SIEGFRIED: My wife and children join me in taking off our hats (figuratively) in appreciation for the generosity and hospitality that we will never be able adequately to reciprocate!

My sincere thanks go as well to the brilliant and pious *Rebbeim* who have touched my life, be they in Jerusalem, Manhattan, Stamford, or Brooklyn. I suspect that in their admirable humility they would forego the recognition; accordingly, I shall not mention them by name. The same can be said for Rabbis across America who constantly assist me, and for friends and students throughout the world who have been nurtured on and who practice every precept of *chessed.*

"Thank you" seems an awfully trite phrase to offer to the Almighty. I have been blessed with life, health, family and sustenance. To the endless list of blessings for which I am grateful can now be added the privilege of bringing this latest volume to press.

For all intents and purposes, my wife wrote this book — with a modest assist from her husband. When I virtually disappeared or was present but unavailable, she, in her inimitable way, was always there.

With the exception of the two biographical pieces in this book ("Crossing the Bridge" and "The French Have a Word for It"), every name and location in this book has been changed to ensure the privacy of the individuals involved. A few minor characters are composites and I have also taken some liberties with chronology. The essence of the stories, however, is true. All the experiences recorded here actually happened, and I have tried to retell them accurately.

It would appear that some readers are the victims of an incurable, if not altogether harmless, affliction of knowing better than the author who his characters "really" are. Since nothing can discourage them from this obsession, it would be useless for me to try to assure them that the names and settings are totally fictitious and products of my own imagination. Nevertheless, I do assert and warn such incorrigible readers that a search for resemblances between my characters and actual persons living or dead is carried out at the considerable risk of perpetuating and aggravating their own affliction.

הנני מסיים סדרת ספרים זו תוך הבעת תקוה
שמילותי יגיעו את לב הקורא אֱלֵי שאיפה לנשגב.

Hanoch Teller

Jerusalem ת"ו

Isru Chag HaSukkos 5751/October 1990

"Why Taxi?"
An Introduction

THE AVERAGE well-built taxi today generates 200 brake horsepower at 4,750 rpm and 270 pound-feet of torque at 4,000 rpm. I confess I have no idea what that means, but I can tell you that to ride in a taxi driven by a cabbie hungry for fares is an experience that mingles exhilaration and terror in equal measure. The sensation is of being shot from a cannon. If you can imagine having a heart attack and enjoying it, you have some idea what the experience is like.

As many of my readers know, *parnasah* considerations keep me on the lecture circuit a good part of the year, traveling to every part of the globe to address audiences. In order to minimize the time away from my family, I am compelled to follow a very tight travel schedule and a crowded itinerary, and as a result very often find myself shuttling from place to place by cab. I've often quipped that I am the world's greatest (perhaps only) expert on taxis. Ask me anything on the subject and I'll be happy to enlighten you, at $1.50 for the first half answer and 25¢ for every answer after that.

Having whiled away so many precious hours, days, weeks of my life in taxicabs, I've had plenty of time to contemplate the actual purpose of my being there. And of that I have always been certain — that there is indeed a purpose. "A taxi is not merely a conveyance, a means to an end," I told myself. "It is an end unto itself, a venue where something significant should take place." But *what*? Maybe I was making too much of it; perhaps it was just meant to be entertaining and relaxing.

I eliminated that possibility in traffic-snarled Manhattan, where "getting there" by taxi ride has become so much less than "half the fun" that I would need to resort to a negative fraction to express it mathematically. The tedium of the journey is whatever the opposite of "leavened" is, exacerbated by the presence of menacing-looking drivers (occasionally) and cacophonous noises blaring from the radio.

As slow-go NYC traffic grinds bumper-to-bumper into a giddy gridlock due to construction, car-swallowing ruts, and cruising road warriors, I sometimes fantasize coming across a herd of dairy cows grazing and lowing along the shoulders of the FDR, or finding that the Avenue of the

Americas has been twisted into a Mobius strip, or that Gomorrah has sprung up just west of Rockefeller Center (this may not be a fantasy), or that a roadblock made of Paskesz candy is barring access to the BQE and I must eat through it in order to proceed, or that the trees of Central Park are performing schottisches and gavottes for my personal delight.

Okay. Scratch entertaining and relaxing. I decided the subject was worthy of a little investigation and research, so I headed for the public library. Soon I knew more than I ever wanted to know about the history of taxis.

Like the various mass transit modes, the taxicab is a descendant of both the hackney, a horse-drawn carriage, and the Parisian "cabriolet," which was a fast, light, two-wheeled chaise also drawn by one horse. Just after the year 1800 cabriolets turned up in London, where the name was quickly shortened to "cab."

The first taxi to appear in America was called "Salom's Electrobat" and it ran on a 900-pound battery, with the passengers riding in front and the driver atop the rear of the vehicle. The maximum speed of these cabs was 15 miles per hour (not much progress in the last century!). The batteries not only proved too heavy for the pneumatic tires, but they also were very expensive and had to be recharged frequently and for eight hours straight. Luckily someone built a better mousetrap.

In 1907, a New Yorker named Harry N. Allen

hailed a hansom cab to take him home from a restaurant. He rode a distance of about three-fourths of a mile, for which he was charged five dollars. Allen was so enraged by this gouging that he vowed to set up a new cab service, one which would charge low rates based on the distance traveled. Before the year was over, he had seven hundred cabs on the streets.

One year later, he retired from the business after his cabbies launched a bloody seven-week strike; but he left to the world a new word: *taxicab*. Allen had equipped his vehicles with a distance-measuring device that the French called "taxi-metre," meaning a meter for measuring the tax, or fare.

Simultaneously, in Chicago more innovations were on the way. John D. Hertz, best remembered for the car rental company which bears his name, was twenty-six years old before he'd ever been in an automobile. But when his young career as a boxing manager dwindled, he embarked on a new one in car sales.

Hertz became outstandingly successful by introducing the concept of trade-ins. The revenue generated by his new method of salesmanship was enormous, but the surplus cars created a tremendous problem for the dealerships. Hertz's solution was to put the second-hand cars to work as taxicabs in a business that he would manage.

Determined to avoid a repetition of the strike that had paralyzed Allen's fleet, he made his drivers partners in the company through a profit-sharing plan and paid them all a commission.

Hertz insisted that the drivers be neatly dressed in a uniform that included a hat and well-shined shoes and puttees. (I wonder how today's taxi union would vote on that.) He provided all kinds of services for his drivers, from medical to legal, and insisted that they do no car repairs themselves, to ensure that no one but specialized mechanics would tinker with his cars.

As soon as Hertz entered the industry, he slashed the taxi rates in half, stopped charging for deadhead mileage, and advertised that he could have a cab at anyone's home within ten minutes. Overnight, taxicabs became a service for the common man as well as the affluent.

From a University of Chicago study, Hertz learned that yellow with a slight tint of red was the most visible color at the greatest distances, so he painted all his taxis yellow. He believed that stop-and-go lights at boulevards would speed up traffic, thereby getting his cabs more quickly to their destinations. To induce the city of Chicago to permit the introduction of traffic lights, he paid for their installation and agreed to remove them if they proved a hindrance. In no time, his costs were reimbursed by the municipality.

Hertz's Yellow Cab Company, with a fleet of twenty-seven hundred cars, entered into a contract with Firestone Tire & Rubber Company for the lease of tires to be paid for on the basis of miles traveled. Firestone was to maintain and repair them, and to this very day the world's largest taxicab fleet has never owned a tire! Another of Yellow Cab's innovations was the development of a hand-operated windshield wiper which was later replaced by automatic wipers.

I hope you found the above information as edifying as I did. But edifying as it was, I remained unenlightened as to the Divine purpose of my magical mystery tours. My library research had not granted me the insight I was seeking.

At this juncture, I had occasion to visit the Jerusalem Department of Motor Vehicles, a story in itself.

Since acquiring a driver's license in Israel is such a tortuous and expensive procedure, *olim* usually try to exchange their foreign driver's license for a valid local one. Unbeknownst to me, this shortcut is possible only within the first two years of one's arrival in Israel.

Well after my first two years had elapsed, I found myself on the horns of a dilemma: I could either attend Israeli driver's ed. classes, theory and practice, investing hundreds of dollars and numerous days, only to fail the test the first time around (as a matter of course), then wait seven weeks for a retest; *or* I could somehow find a way to circumvent the two-year statute of limitations. As you may have guessed, I opted for the latter.

Execution of such a plan stands a chance of success only if it's fortified with Vitamin P. But no such nutrients did I possess: No friends or relatives of mine were employed by the Transport Ministry. I couldn't even locate a relative of a cleaning lady at Jerusalem's DMV who could provide the necessary *protektzia*. Discouraged but not defeated, I decided to take my problem to the top — the Minister of Transportation himself.

As outrageous as this may sound, in Israel, where almost nothing is outrageous, government officials are notoriously accessible to the proletariat. Two boxes of chocolate (really!) and a press card (that's another story) brought me to a position only two secretaries removed from the inner sanctum. All I had to do was wait my turn.

Among the other turn-waiters in the oak-paneled reception area was the head honcho of Israel's Taxi Commission who had come to plead his case for raising taxi fares. Not that I recognized him; one of our fellow waiters did and he took the opportunity to attack the head honcho's apparently well-known stand. A minor melee ensued and I did what I could to keep the peace; i.e., I did not get involved. An officious secretary took it upon herself to referee the slanging match and soon the contenders had repaired to their corners, their seconds fanning them with copies of *Yediot Acharonot* and pouring bottles of Tempo Cola down their throats.

I snatched the opportunity (before the bell signaling Round 2 rang) to offer Israel's Mr. Taxi my humble opinion, as a citizen and patron, of the proposed fare hike. He responded with, I thought, admirable restraint.

"*Chabibi*," he said, "there's no such thing as a free lunch. If you value your time, and a taxi enables you to use it more effectively, you should have no objection to paying a little extra for the privilege. When you get into a cab, you enter into a verbal contract with the driver, saying, in effect: 'Take me where I want to go more rapidly and comfortably than I could get there by other means, and I'll cover the cost.' You gain from the convenience; why should the driver take a loss? Besides, half the passengers are on an expense account, so why should they care if it costs the boss a shekel more or less?"

Mr. Taxi's speech left me speechless. His words made the "Off Duty" light in my brain flicker as I quickly shifted gears from neutral to drive. All at once I knew I had gained the insight I had so eagerly sought.

It was not the *taxi* that was meaningful, I realized, but the *fare*. The analogy to life was obvious: The ticking taximeter registers the passage of the time allotted us on this earth and the price we must pay for it. The more smoothly we travel down life's highways and byways, the cheaper the cost per mile; but the unit price increases dramatically with every traffic jam, detour and roadblock we encounter. If the purpose of our ride is to benefit others, that is, if our road is paved with *mitzvos* and *chessed*, it will be smooth sailing all the way. Still, life is not a "free lunch" — we all have to pay our way, but we have the means to keep the cost down.

Rabbi Chaim Shmuelevitz often quoted Rabbi Yisrael Salanter's analogy comparing life in this world to a sojourn in a deluxe hotel, where even a small glass of water can cost ten dollars. The only way to afford life's exorbitant expenses and still remain solvent is by operating on an "expense account." At the end of our hotel stay, we pay the bill, then hand over the receipts to the Boss of Bosses and He reimburses us. Only those deserving of such a perk are awarded "expense accounts," and only the justifiable outlays are "reimbursed."

The part of Mr. Taxi's oratory that really fuel-injected my imagination and lubricated my valves was the "verbal contract with the driver," that sometimes anonymous, often aggravating, always quickly forgotten person charged with the awesome responsibility of conveying human cargo safely from place to place. Instantly I refocused the object of my researches.

Our Sages teach that one should rise in deference to the elderly, be he Jew or Gentile, because he "has witnessed so many events and occurrences in his lifetime." His vast experiences automatically endow him with wisdom worthy of our respect. Taxi drivers, by virtue of their grand-scale exposure to a genuine cross-section of humanity, likewise have witnessed a great deal in their lifetimes and likewise are worthy of our respect.

Like the *baal agalah*, the wagondriver protagonist of many Chassidic tales, the taxi driver has much to teach us. Not for naught does the *baal agalah* figure so prominently in so many popular stories. He is both the central character and the vehicle by which we, the audience, *together* with the wagon passenger, journey away from our mundane, predictable environment. Once we have distanced ourselves from our past (be it geographic or metaphysical), we can embark on an adventure in the company of this total stranger, with our defenses down and our minds receptive to the wisdom he can impart.

It is the Omniscient Dispatcher who matches the cabbie with his fare, not mere happenstance that throws these two together. In a crowded bus or a jammed subway train, each individual is really all alone; most often, the passengers exchange not a single word with their fellows. In a taxicab, there is partnership, that which the Taxi Commissioner dubbed the "verbal contract." However, if we close our hearts and minds to the cab driver's Providential presence in our *dalet ammos*, we forego a God-given, golden opportunity to learn what might turn out to be the most important lesson of our lives.

From the moment I made up my mind to pay more attention to my cab drivers, I discovered a veritable font of information and a vast resource of mitzvah opportunities. The following are some amazing "taxi stories" from the past year alone:

Dateline Miami: My driver from Fort Lauderdale/Hollywood International Airport was an elderly fellow who looked as if he should have been at poolside in a retirement condo rather than behind the wheel in a traffic jam. His wrinkles were a roadmap of his travels and woes. "Why so down?" I asked.

Joe glanced in his rearview mirror and looked me over. (One thing I've learned in my life is the value of never trying to conceal my Judaism.

Wherever I go, in any part of the world, I dress as I would at home in Jerusalem: my *kippah* or hat, my suit, my beard. I've never been mistaken for a non-Jew, and many people sit up and take notice when they see a Jew, or fellow Jew, walk proudly by. My Jewish appearance is often the key that unlocks long-sealed doors. At the same time, it tends to make *me* more careful in my actions.) Back to Joe, who was looking me over. When he was sure that my interest was genuine, he began to tell me his tale. An ex-Lower East Sider, he was now semi-retired and, true to my initial assessment, lived in a senior citizens' condo.

"When I was a kid," Joe began, "in our house Shabbos was Shabbos, know what I mean? I even went to yeshivah for a coupla years, till my Bar Mitzvah. But a lotta us guys didn't want no parta all that old-fashion stuff — we was Americans now, capital A. Mama and Papa was, you know, simple people. They also wanted me to be an American, but I think they had no idea then how you can be an American and also be a religious Jew. So when I told them I was quittin yeshivah and goin to public school, they were kinda happy and sad at the same time. By the time Esther and me got married, Papa was already gone and there wasn't nothin Mama could say about Esther bein from a non-religious family."

This was an old story; I had heard it so many times before, but it never ceased to sadden me. I knew what came next, even before Joe told me. He and Esther had a small business, a toy store, on the Lower East Side, and they made a decent living. They gave their only son, Daniel, "everything"

— excluding a Jewish education — and Dan fulfilled the American Dream.

"He's a 'sanitation engineer' — that's what I call
him cause his whole life is garbage. It took me a
long time to see that. All I could see was that my
son, a first-generation American, got a college
degree, a fancy job in a bank, big house on Long
Island, two cars — late model, naturally, and a set
of fishin tackle like he was goin after Moby Dick
all by hisself. Every wall of his you should excuse
me *den* has got a dead fish nailed on it, or a snap-
shot of Dan posin with some famous fish he
caught, in a fancy-Delancey frame. Danny is so
American he could be a WASP. So why am I com-
plainin? I'll tell you why."

I knew he would.

"A coupla years back, me and Esther was
gonna go to Israel for the first time. We're all excited, right? We had just retired and bought this
condo here and everythin we did was like an adventure, you know? Then, two days before we're
suppose to leave, *pow!* Mama dies. I say maybe we
should cancel, but Esther is so disappointed, so I
ask my Rabbi in the Reform temple we joined
down here, and he says since we already got our
tickets, we'll lose money if we cancel. Also, he
says, if we dedicate our trip to Mama's memory,
it'll be a mitzvah to go, and if we give a donation to
the temple, it'll be an even bigger mitzvah. So
whaddaya think? We went.

"My Rabbi gives me this 'mourner's badge' to
wear for the week of *shivah* and on the plane some
of these yeshivah guys ask me what it is, a medal,

maybe? An award for somethin? I figure they're really dumb if they don't know from *shivah*, but it turns out they *do* know from *shivah*, and a lot better than me. Would you believe it, total strangers and they all get up to make a *minyan* for me so I can say *kaddish*!

"Anyway, I say it's the least we can do to repay them if me and Esther spend some time with them in Jerusalem. Was I ever wrong! Esther said afterwards it was like we was starvin to death all these years and we didn't even know it! In those two weeks, they gave us more than we could ever pay back: They gave us our *neshamah*s.

"So when we get home, all excited, we go straight to Danny and Jennifer — that's our daughter-in-law — and tell them all about it. So, whaddaya think? They look at us like we're crazy. They start talkin about puttin us in a home! We had a big fight — all right, a war. For eight years they 'maintained radio silence,' like they say in the old submarine movies. Now, once a year, we talk on the phone. Big deal. But they won't step foot in our house cause we're too Jewish for them, and we can't go there cause we only eat kosher and they only eat *treif*. It's like a religion with them. So, that's the story. Sixty-eight years I'm on this earth, and pretty soon I'm gonna be *in* this earth, and what am I gonna leave behind? A 'sanitation engineer' who uses dead fish for wallpaper."

"Are there any grandchildren?" I asked him casually.

Joe slammed on the brakes. I slid off the bench

and whacked my head against the back of the front seat. Horns honked all around us as other drivers squealed to a halt. But Joe was euphoric. "That's it! Scot!" he exclaimed.

"Huh?" was about all I could manage.

"You won't mind if I make a quick stop, right?" Before I could answer, he veered left across four lanes of traffic and pulled up in front of a multi-storied condo. My jaw was still gaping as he flew out the door at a speed that belied his years, ran into the building, and returned a few minutes later with, I gathered, Esther in tow. They got into the front seat and Joe started driving, I hoped to my destination, all the while speaking animatedly to his wife about his terrific plan. I might have been invisible, for all the attention they gave me.

"So we'll tell them it's our Bar Mitzvah present to Scottie," Joe was saying. "How can they refuse? We can even make a side trip to Europe or some-thin, so they won't think somethin fishy's goin on." Joe and Esther grinned at each other over the inadvertent pun. "And when we get to Jerusalem, we'll look up those yeshivah guys..."

Luckily, the car knew the way to my destination all by itself, since it seemed to be getting little help from its driver, who was otherwise engaged. When we arrived at the Jewish Community Center where I was to speak, I hesitated to interrupt the plenary session in progress up front, but I had to pay my fare. Joe was way ahead of me.

"I don't want your money, sonny," he said. "I want your address. Me and Esther heard you speak the last time you were in Miami. Thought I didn't know who you were, huh? Well, when we come to Israel with Scot in a coupla months, we're gonna look you up too!"

And they did.

Dateline London: I was feeling a little uneasy when I got a good look at my youthful dark-complected driver and read his unusual name off the ID card, but when Mustafa Basargan greeted me with a wide, toothy grin and a hearty "*Shalom aleichem!*" my adrenaline level dropped down to normal. I returned the greeting and he asked me what had brought me to the UK.

"I'm giving a lecture on Jewish observance, at St. John's Wood. But what brought *you* to the British Isles?"

Mustafa, it turned out, was an Iranian Jew who had sought political asylum in England during the recent Iran-Iraq war. He explained that since it was a "holy war" and Jews in Iran are considered "unholy," but not unholy enough to be exempt from army service, they are assigned the unholiest military duties in battle. "Such as?" I asked, thinking he meant KP and latrine.

"Such as walking ahead of the troops to see if there are being landmines," Mustafa clarified. Eventually, he was promoted from kamikaze duty to a slightly less risky task, or so he thought. Along with a platoon of other youngsters like himself, he had to charge at the enemy at point-blank range.

"This was less risky than landmines?" I asked.

"Most certainly," Mustafa replied. "The whole platoon was being issued holy keys for wearing around our neck. Holy keys to unlock the gates of Heaven. Iranian boys are thinking this is pretty good deal: If they are dying bravely in battle, they are already having guaranteed pass to spiritual afterlife." What convinced Mustafa that something was rotten in Teheran was the holy inscription engraved on the holy key: MADE IN TAIWAN.

The plucky little Persian sold his key to a crippled beggar boy for the mendicant's wooden leg. "He is not needing it, really, since he is not really being crippled." Mustafa bent down and retrieved the rough wooden bat from under his seat. "It is making good cosh for passengers who are not wanting to pay!" he said, flashing his ivories at me in the mirror.

I felt this was a good time to get my fare ready. As he handed me my change, Mustafa dropped one more pearl. "Besides, what am I needing made-in-Taiwan key to Heaven for, when I am having real key with me since always?" He flipped open the glove compartment and took out a small *Tanach,* which he kissed with Persian passion. "And this one is not being made in Taiwan!"

Dateline New York: The driver who picked me up at Penn Station was an Israeli and I could see right away that the storm windows were up. An Israeli doesn't need an opening, so I said nothing but "*Shalom*" and settled back in my seat, ready to receive an earful. It wasn't long in coming.

"It would never happen in Jerusalem!" he fumed. "Not even in Tel Aviv!" Two hours earlier, he had stopped at a red light and an inner city kid had tapped on the window on the passenger's side and asked directions. Yoram gave them to him, but the kid made like he couldn't hear, so Yoram leaned over to open the window. Just as he did so, the kid's confederate reached in the driver's open window and relieved Yoram of the wad of bills folded in his shirt pocket. Then the two sneaker-boys took off like Olympic runners on steroids and were gone before the light had changed.

Yoram had a few choice words in several familiar languages for these skillful rip-off artists. Considering the altitude of his dander, however, I wasn't about to point out that, despite the object lesson, his more recent earnings were once again resting temptingly in the same shirt pocket. Instead I offered my sympathies and we exchanged personal histories.

Midtown traffic was heavy so I had plenty of time to learn that Yoram and family were honest-to-goodness *yordim* (not the "student-type" who is planning to return home "soon"), living in Queens. They were debating the wisdom of enrolling their children in the local Jewish Day School, after having sent them to public school for several years. "In Israel," he said, "you can go to public school and still know you are *Yehudi — ata meivin?*" I *meivin*ed. "Here, you go to public school, pretty soon you think you are *Portoricani.*"

"You're right," I said. "A Jewish education is the most important thing a Jewish parent can give his child."

"But it's *hamon kessef*," Yoram lamented. "And what if they become *dati!* Hello *payot*; goodbye *kadduregel* on *Shabbat!*" Yoram was not what you might call subtle, but I've taken worse insults and survived.

"Better *payot* than *Portoricani* grandchildren, don't you think?" I offered. Yoram let go of the wheel, Israeli-style, and turned around to look at me more closely. I was too busy steering vicariously to interpret the expression on his face, but I did notice it wasn't altogether unfriendly.

We stopped at a light (Yoram's hands were back on the wheel — *phew!*) and up ahead, about ten cars away, we saw a reenactment of Yoram's rip-off in progress. The driver of that Yellow, an Oriental, was climbing out of his cab with a look of consternation and the two sneaker-boys were charging down the street, darting through traffic — headed right in our direction!

"That's them!" Yoram shouted, and simultaneously we each threw our door open, scoring direct hits. I couldn't believe it! I'm not a violent person, as anyone who knows me will testify, and I don't think I've ever struck someone intentionally in my life. I'd like to believe that I was only opening my door to get out and try to catch one of the thieves, but I'd be lying if I said I didn't feel a surge of satisfaction at seeing those punks spreadeagled on the pavement, the wind knocked out of them.

The Oriental driver and Yoram divvied up the contents of the punks' pockets, bowed to the cheering crowd on the sidewalk (honest!), shook hands and got back in the saddle. We galloped off into the sunset.

To top off a coincidence-filled day, Providence had arranged for me to be speaking at the very Day School in Queens that Yoram had been considering for his children. Wordlessly, he dismounted along with me and together we moseyed on into the principal's office.

Dateline Detroit: Two taxis pulled up at my feet in response to my frantic arm-waving. The stars were beginning to twinkle and I was running late, but I would have preferred walking to getting in the middle of a cabbie slug-out. The dark-skinned driver of Black-and-White 1 (the local equivalent of Yellow) got out and strolled over to Black-and-White 2 to have a word with the driver. In moments, Black-and-White 2 proved that even a 1983 Buick can do zero-to-sixty in point-eight seconds, given the proper incentive.

That this made me uneasy would be an understatement. But the minute hand on my watch ticking closer and closer to the appointed hour of my lecture made me even uneasier. I vacillated.

"Hop aboord, mon," the seven-foot, gladiatorial Haitian driver of Black-and-White 1 invited graciously, and the decision was out of my hands.

"Yoo know," he said, "I hod a reeson for wanting dees fare." I tried desperately to remember some manly art of self-defense. My mind was a blank. "Yoo see, I cood tell yoo were a Jooish mon." Even the words of the *Shema* wouldn't come to mind. "I hahve a Jooish problem, ond I t'ought may bee yoo cahn help mee."

Oh. "Shoot," I said, and quickly bit my tongue. "I mean, go right ahead and ask. I'll do whatever I can to help."

In his rich, mellifluous patois, the Haitian explained that although cab driving was his full-time night profession, he sunlighted as a janitor by day in a building with many "Jooish" tenants. They treated him very well and one old "mon" in particular, "with a little block hot like yoors," had been a real friend. "Thees morning, he die," the driver said sadly. The old man's son had come to claim the body and make arrangements.

"I told him hees dahd ond mee was good friends ond I want to go to de fyooneral, bot hee say hee cahn't bee boddered, hee's gonna hahve Dahd cremated tomorrow." The janitor-driver thought this was a "bahd ting," so he had asked the other tenants if they were willing to chip in with him for a proper burial and they had all agreed. The problem now was to convince the son that cremation was against Jewish law. "Hee's ahn ignorant one, dat mon."

Needless to say, I was happy to oblige — right after my lecture. It was the least I could do for a fellow Jew and for a Gentile anxious to perform *chessed shel emes.*

Dateline Goethals Bridge: Mario Francioso picked me up at Newark Airport and floored me even before he floored the accelerator. "*Nu, vu* *geist du?"* he demanded in a sullen, aggressive voice. I knew I was onto a good story here, but Mario's manifest ill humor dampened my enthusiasm for conversation. Reflexively, I responded to his hostile greeting with some hostility of my own and gave him the address in Yiddish, certain the Italian's command of the language was limited to that four-word greeting.

I was wrong. Mario took off like a shot, and in the right direction. Every now and then, he hurled another angry query at me over his shoulder, in somewhat more fluent Yiddish than I can boast of, but still I contained my curiosity. The set of his burly back, the crease of his brow, the grim down-turned mouth all screamed "Keep Out — Private Property. Trespassers Will Be Executed."

We cruised along the Staten Island Expressway more or less in silence until I remembered the lesson I had been drilling into my students for over a decade. "You owe someone who provides a service more than his fee," I had told them. "You owe him human decency. The price isn't paid in full until you have said 'Thank you' to him, or, even better, until you've shown genuine interest in his well-being." It was time I practiced what I had preached.

"Are you all right, Mr. Francioso?" I asked — in English. "Is something troubling you?"

Mario glanced at me suspiciously from the corner of his eye. Then, all at once, the floodgates opened and Mario poured out a heart-rending tale of sorrow. He had two sons, both "bums," as he put it — the elder doing hard time for armed robbery, the younger doing hard drugs. His three daughters were married to "bums" of a different sort and, according to Dad, "woulda bin bedder off ifn dey got divorced but dey can't, bein as how dey's Roman Catlics, like." He kissed the crucifix dangling from his neck.

Mario's litany had only begun. "It'sa good ting Celia — dat's der mudder — is dead an buried or dis *tzuris* woulda kilt huh."

First Yiddish; now Jewish humor. What gives? I wondered.

Celia had taken a long time dying, and every penny they had trying not to. By the time she'd shuffled off her mortal coil, Mario was triple-mortgaged and "inta de shahks fuh twenny gees. My whole take-home goes t' jus de vigorish." Freely translated, his entire income went to paying the "loan sharks" usurious interest on his $20,000 loan without diminishing his debt at all.

This was heavy *tzuris*, all right, and there wasn't much I could do besides sympathize.

" 'Ey, it's okay!" Mario consoled me. "Youse don' gotta take it so poisonal, like. But ya know, I feel a lot bedder now, jus tawkin about it. I also know what I gotta do — I gotta swalla my pride an go t' Uncle Moishie. He's loaded an he likes me. He'll gimme de dough, sure."

Uncle Moishie? Of "Mitzvah Men" fame? I must have missed something. Mario noticed my confusion and guffawed heartily.

"My mudder's brudder," he explained. "Din I

tellya my mudder was Jewish? 'Ey, maybe ya know de guy — Moish Cohen from Canarsie?"

So *that's* where Mario's Yiddish fluency came from. "I have a little news flash for you, Mr. Francioso," I said. "If your mother was Jewish, then according to Jewish law, so are you."

"'Ey, youse de second poison t' tell me dat. I had dese Jewish goils in my cab a coupla munts back. Good kids, I picked 'em up at de airpawt. Tole me der teacha in Israel said dey should always be nice t' anybody who provides a soivice — even a dumb hack like me!"

I spent the better part of a year collecting "taxi stories," and when I realized I had so many of them that I could fill a book, well... I did. The stories contained herein were all told to me either by cabbies or by fellow passengers sharing the ride with me as well as a tale worth repeating. I found them inspiring; I hope you will, too.

Ticket to Ride

I DON'T WANT TO LEAVE; the yeshivah is my life!"

"But now your life has changed. Tomorrow, the Communists will close this yeshivah, too. Anyone found here will be arrested. You've got to leave."

"But what about Rebbe?" Dovid Mandel asked his beloved teacher. "Where are you going to run?"

"Run? I'm too old to run, and too proud of my life to hide. I will be here when they come!"

"Can't I stay with you?" Dovid pleaded. "I may be able to run errands or help out in some way."

Reb Lazer shook his head. Over the last few hours, he had spoken privately to every student in his small yeshivah. In the interest of security, each had been told to make plans and not reveal them to the others, and each had responded with the same request. They would rather stay with their mentor and be incarcerated than flee the yeshivah and their Torah lifestyle.

Reb Lazer took his prize student by the hand. "May Hashem bless you and watch over you. I am sure you will make the yeshivah proud, and provide a merit for your parents, of blessed memory. But you must go!"

"Where? How? I have no money, no food, no clothing! And no family to go *to*!"

"Money, food, clothing — these are things that come and go. In life, you need only one thing: trust in God. All you must do is internalize the thought, '*Ein od Milvado*' — there is nothing other than Hashem! Equipped with that knowledge you will not want for anything else. Now, try to catch the train that runs from Lubni through Kiev. Maybe things are safer in the big city.

"When you reach Kiev, locate this address." The Rebbe pressed a scrap of paper in Dovid's palm. "There you will find all the family you will ever need — *my* family."

"But..."

"I'm afraid there is nothing more to say," Reb Lazer cut him off abruptly, fighting the tears that were forcing their way into his eyes. "Leave!"

Dovid Mandel took one long last look at his Rebbe. Then he hugged him as tightly as any son ever hugged his father, and quickly departed, stopping at the holy ark to give a final kiss to the *paroches*. As he strode out along the familiar stone floor, Dovid thrummed his fingers over the wooden tables of the clandestine Tailor's *Shul* which had been his *beis midrash* and home for the past four years. He had studied its books, slept on its benches, and swept its floors. His mind told him that he had to leave, never to return to this hallowed hall, but his heart denied it.

"I'll come back," he promised himself. "As soon as I can, I'll come back."

Dovid stepped out of the quiet, misty *shul* into the street. For a few minutes, he stood transfixed, blinded as much by the bright sunlight as by his own churning thoughts.

DOVID MANDEL was seventeen years old. Yet, in those seventeen years, he had lived what felt like a thousand lifetimes. His parents had been poor Jews who lived in a small village outside of Lubni. Like many other righteous and devout Jews of that time, they had sacrificed everything to raise their son as a learned Jew.

When it became apparent that they could no longer fulfill his needs, they sent him to Lubni to live with his uncle. He was eight years old when he left home.

His uncle, a bachelor, treated his nephew more like an adult than a child. If Dovid played, he was foolish. If he slept, he was lazy. If he laughed, he was silly. Dovid learned early on that a carefree childhood was something that only other children had. For him, there was no such thing as the innocence of youth, only the responsibilities of adulthood.

Not long after Dovid left home, a priest from his hometown accused the Jews of one crime or another. Justice and holy retribution were not long in coming and the Mandels senior were caught up in the wake. At the age of ten, little Dovid was truly alone.

After two years, Dovid could no longer remain with his uncle. For the next three years, he wandered from one house, one town and one *beis midrash* to another. Dovid adjusted quickly to his lot and role in Jewish destiny. Wherever he went and wherever he was sent, he tried his hardest to fit in, until it was time to move on.

The situation had changed when he met the pious Reb Lazer from the town of Lubavitch. The kabbalists explain that the souls of friends can be indeed closer than the souls of blood relatives, but this Rebbe and *talmid* never needed a mystical explanation to explain their relationship. Reb Lazer was the father Dovid had always wanted but had never really had. To the caring Rebbe, Dovid was the consummate fulfillment of the Rabbinic dictum, "Students: behold they are like sons."

Their extremely close relationship, cemented in Torah learning and bonded in Chassidic teaching, was now coming to an abrupt close. In just a little while a train would carry him down the road to an unknown future. His Rebbe's words echoed loudly in his ears: "*Ein od*...there is nothing other than Hashem!"

IN 1924, Russia was descending into the clutches of history's greatest murderer, a madman determined to re-create the empire of the Czars — and more. Josef Stalin was a ruthless peasant who became a tyrannical despot as the dictator of the Soviet Union. Under his leadership, tragedy and suffering were the inevitable outcome of his designs for a state of the proletariat.

During Stalin's reign of terror, millions of innocent people, including many Torah-loving Jews, disappeared. Some were sent to the gulag, others to prisons no less demonic, while others were murdered outright or committed to asylums for the insane, their identities liquidated, their names purged from the pages of history. A special division of the secret police was devoted to those remaining Jews who still believed more in the Almighty in Heaven than in the State on Earth. For those who survived, life was often worse than death, as they were forced to "testify" against their relatives and friends.

Most of the boys in Reb Lazer's yeshivah knew the risks they were taking by learning in the Tailor's *Shul*. Even Reb Lazer talked about it. For them, it wasn't a matter of whether or not they would be caught, but *when*.

In those insane times, not every Communist who claimed to be a rabid anti-Semite *was* one. Many joined the ranks of the Jewish section of the Communist Party for ideological or pragmatic reasons; a few of these pragmatists, with a spark of Jewish sentiment still glowing in their hearts, used their position to save lives, rather than to take them. Occasionally, they would warn their fellow Jews of trouble that was brewing.

Ironically, the warning that was given to Reb Lazer came from his own son — a son Dovid had never even known existed. But while Reb Lazer's son could be relied upon for a warning, he could not provide protection. And so the venerable Rabbi had no recourse but to disband the yeshivah he had fought so long to maintain.

With a prayer on his lips, Reb Lazer gazed wistfully at his student running toward the train depot. The Rebbe then turned sadly from the window and began gathering *sefarim* to be hidden until the storm of Communism had passed.

THE TRAIN STATION was jammed with travelers of every size, shape and description. Mothers and children, elderly couples, Russian soldiers and civil servants, well-dressed business people, farmers and peasants. One segment of the population, however, was conspicuous by its absence: religious Jewish boys of military age.

Trembling with fear, Dovid approached the ticket window. "Can you tell me how much a ticket to Kiev costs?" he asked.

"Four rubles."

"What am I going to do?" Mandel thought. "Maybe I can borrow the money... but who would lend it to me? Maybe I could lie to the conductor and tell him I had a ticket but misplaced it. No, he'd never believe me. Maybe I could just hide and hope he misses me."

Dovid's thoughts were interrupted by a shrill

whistle from the steam engine. Everyone around him was moving toward the edge of the platform, readying themselves to board the train. Dovid could see the huge locomotive coming ever-closer, looming into view. "There must be a place for me on that train!" he thought. "But where?"

SUDDENLY, he spotted two well-dressed gentlemen speaking Yiddish to each other. They had an air of success and confidence about them that was as manifest as the newness of their suits. Without knowing anything about them other than their self-important appearance and their self-indulgent mannerisms, Dovid figured they were on their way to Kiev on official business. The young lad approached them with hope in his eyes and fear in his heart.

"E-e-excuse me," he said hesitantly.

"Yes, what do you want?" one of the men answered coldly.

Dovid's answer rushed out uncontrollably. "I must leave town and I have no ticket. Could you please help me?"

Both men stared at Dovid. "You have no ticket? Then how can we help? This train is already booked. Wait for the next one. Maybe it will have room."

"But I have no money, either," Dovid confessed to them.

The two men eyed each other smugly. "That's the trouble with you boys. You spend your time secretly looking into books, instead of looking out for yourselves. You have no money and you have no ticket. Well, I suppose if we can't give you one, we can give you the other. Alexi, give the poor boy a few kopeks and I will do the same."

"But a ticket is four rubles!"

"Sergei, did you hear that? What impudence!"

Sergei obviously agreed. "So you don't like what we give? Then you get nothing! Get away, before we call the police!"

"I'm sorry, I didn't mean to imply..." Startled at their brusque manner, Dovid found himself backing off... and backing up. Unwittingly, he backed right into an elderly lady carrying four overstuffed bags, filled to overflowing with loaves of black bread and assorted *shmattes*.

"EEEKKKKK!" Her bags, bread and clothing went scattering in all directions.

"Oh-h! F-forgive me!" Dovid apologized. He began rapidly to pick up the loaves and rags, helping as much as he could to restore her bags and her dignity. In seconds the wind gust from the approaching train would send her *shmattes* all over the platform and onto the tracks.

"Why don't you watch where you're going?" she scolded.

"I'm sorry."

"You're sorry? Is that all you have to say?" she accused. "Aren't you going to ask if I'm hurt?"

"Are you hurt?" Dovid responded dutifully.

"No! And no thanks to you. You almost killed me. A few more steps, and I would have fallen onto the train tracks."

"I didn't mean to bump into you. It was just that I... "

"You weren't looking where you were going," she interrupted, finishing the sentence for him.

DOVID LOOKED at his victim. She was in her mid-sixties and dressed like a peasant. Wayward strands of her gray hair peeked out from the edges of a colored scarf. Her face and features were etched with wrinkles, but she still had the warmth and good humor of the little girl that must still be inside somewhere. She looked Jewish, but then again Dovid wasn't sure. Maybe she was just another Russian peasantwoman.

"Can I trust her?" he thought to himself. "What if she hates Jews? What if she turns me over to the police?"

"All aboard!" the conductor cried.

Panic-stricken, Dovid looked around for help. A wave of humanity began streaming into the four cars that followed the engine. Paralyzed for but an instant by the situation, he took a deep breath and then imitated his comrades on all sides, pushing, shoving, and shouting their way onto the train. Before the masses could even settle into whatever position they were going to sit or stand in for the next several hours, the train lurched forward and started moving. Slowly at first, then faster and faster, it picked up speed. Dovid stared at the people around him. They were all busily involved in their own worlds, their own problems, or were busy looking at nowhere. Dovid's eyes came to rest on the grandmotherly looking woman.

"If I don't do something fast, I'll be thrown off this train, possibly even arrested," he thought nervously. Strengthened by Reb Lazer's farewell message, Dovid decided to take action. "I'll have to take the chance. But to be safe, I'll ask her in Yiddish. That way, if she doesn't understand, at least I won't be in any more trouble than I'm in now."

DOVID EDGED CLOSER to the lady and began telling her what had happened since his meeting with Reb Lazer that morning. He didn't actually mean to, but once he started, it was impossible to stop. She looked at him uncomprehendingly as Dovid's entire life story came tumbling out. How he was orphaned at ten. How he shlepped from home to home and from town to town. How he finally found a place where he could live and learn. And now, how he had been told that, in order to continue, he must leave. He finished in a torrent of words and embarrassing tears, explaining that he had neither a ticket nor any money at all.

When he was done, the old woman just looked at him blankly. After what seemed to Dovid like an eternity, she pulled out her ticket and stared at it. Then she asked him in Russian, "Does this go to Kiev?"

"Yes, it does, but..." Dovid tried to get some reaction from her, some advice, or better yet, some help. The only response he got, however, was a vacant stare.

He tried to restate his case, but before he could, the old woman took her precious ticket and asked the person next to her, "Excuse me, is this good for Kiev?"

"Yes, yes," said the fellow traveler impatiently.

"Thank you," she bowed. Then she directed her attention to the person sitting on the other side, and began all over again. "Will this pass take me all the way to Kiev?"

"Yes, it will."

THE OLD WOMAN stood up. Dovid's eyes grew wide as she proceeded to survey each of the sixty-odd passengers who were crammed into their car. "Can you tell me where this ticket goes?"

"Kiev! Can't you read?" growled one noncommissioned army officer.

"Are you sure?" she asked a lady twenty passengers back.

"Of course!"

By now, everyone was staring and glaring at the attraction. Some of the crowd was amused; in very few did she arouse any pity. Dovid was exceedingly vexed. "Heaven help me! The one person I tell my troubles to is a lunatic. Now what do I do?"

DOVID DIDN'T HAVE a lot of time to cogitate or engage in crisis management, for at that very moment the conductor entered the car and began collecting tickets. He was a tall, heavy-set man with a ruddy face and a voice that bellowed authority. "Tickets! I must have your tickets!" Obediently, one passenger after another pressed the stub into his meaty palm.

Dovid nervously searched in his empty pockets. His hands were trembling, his palms and forehead sweating profusely. There was no hope that the conductor would let him stay on the train; there was no possibility he would stop the train to let him off. Already he began to ache all over in anticipation of being hurled bodily from the moving car.

Mandel's mind was racing. In a few moments the conductor would gruffly demand his pass. He would begin to explain, but before he would get very far the conductor would grab him by the throat, drag him through the car to the door. Pleading and begging for mercy would get him nowhere. Dovid's life began to flash before his eyes as swiftly as the fast-moving tracks below.

With a curse and a shove, the conductor would heave him overboard. If he was lucky, he would land on the grass somewhere, breaking perhaps only both his legs, a hand, and several vertebrae, while suffering dozens of miscellaneous cuts and bruises and ending up with a massive concussion, which would more than likely cause him to be permanently brain damaged.

Alternatively, he would die a horrible death,

mangled and crushed under many tons of iron and steel until his body was mauled grotesquely beyond recognition.

"At the rate he's moving through the crowd," Dovid calculated, "I have a minute or two until my trip — and probably my life — is over." The crowded aisle afforded little resistance to the trainman experienced at maneuvering himself through a horde as quickly as possible. Dovid pushed himself desperately to the farthest extreme of the car. His heart pounding as though it would explode, he scanned the peoplescape, searching in vain for some camouflage by which to conceal himself. Suddenly, through the window of the door Dovid saw another conductor approaching his car from the opposite end. The man was a virtual clone of the one closing in on him from the other side.

MEANWHILE, the old lady had concluded her deranged exhibition and wound up alongside Dovid. As Dovid exchanged places with her in the mobbed aisle, he forced a polite but fear-frozen smile. "This might be the last chance I ever get to do the mitzvah of honoring the elderly," he thought grimly to himself. She smiled back and said, "My ticket is good for Kiev," and tauntingly stuck it in his face. She then grinned a foolish, toothless grin and let her precious ticket drop from sight. Pushing her way past Dovid, he could feel her hand roughly take hold of his. A piece of stiff paper passed between them.

The old woman moved on toward the massive

frame of the conductor. "Ticket, lady," he bellowed at her.

From behind him, Dovid heard a half-scream/half-shriek that could have awakened the dead. "My ticket! I lost it! It was here a minute ago!" the woman cried.

The conductor just continued to stare at her, unbelievingly.

"On the grave of my holy ancestors," the old lady swore and spat on the conductor's brightly polished shoes. "I had a ticket. It was right here in my hand. But it disappeared. Didn't I have a rail pass?" she asked the person standing next to her.

"Yes, conductor, I saw it with my own eyes," a witness volunteered.

"Me, too," said another passenger.

"She probably dropped it," said a third.

"My rail pass!" she howled again. "It must be here." In a panic, she began emptying out the contents of all four bags: loaves of bread, assorted vegetables and clothing tumbled out onto the floor and the nearby passengers. She began tossing items in all directions. A red kerchief landed on the conductor's hat.

"Leave her alone," one of the passengers shouted. "Can't you see she's nuts!"

"She's mad! Let her be," cried another.

By this time, the conductor had ample evidence not to dispute their claim. "*Vsey v porjadke, vsey v porjadke*, it's okay," he soothed. "I believe you!"

"Yes, but it must be here somewhere. I know I had it. Didn't I have it? Didn't I?" she asked those around her.

"Yes, yes," they all replied.

"Calm down. I'm sure you'll find it," the conductor said. "Don't worry, I believe you."

"Are you sure, officer?"

"Yes, yes. I'm sure. You just relax. No one will bother you."

"Oh, you're so kind," she smiled at him and gently lifted her red scarf from his hat. The people started laughing and pretty soon the conductor's face was as red as the scarf which had graced him.

"Pardon me," he excused himself and went back to shouting his way down the aisle. "TICKETS! I MUST HAVE YOUR TICKETS!"

In less than a minute, the conductor had worked his way up to Dovid, who was next in line. Bracing himself to stabilize his quivering body, he handed the conductor his precious pass, and resumed breathing.

Dovid edged his way back to his small niche in the corner and then searched through the crowd for the old lady. Their eyes met and she acknowledged his look with a wink. Involuntarily he found himself humming the tune Reb Lazer had taught him to "*Ein od Milvado*." For the first time since early in the morning, Dovid knew things were going to work out after all.

Heard from: Leibel Estrin

Savta

AFTER ELEVEN HOURS of sleepless flying, cramped seats, and plastic foods, all the recent arrivals were eager to clear passport control, pick up their luggage and be on their way. All, that is, except one. Luba Czermak moved with deliberate steps, in no apparent hurry to leave Ben Gurion Airport. She carried an oversized totebag, the strap slung over her shoulder, and one small suitcase that had been stowed under her seat on the plane. Since these two were all she had brought, Luba was able to bypass the luggage carousel altogether. The few seasoned travelers who were similarly unencumbered strode purposefully toward the exit. But not Luba.

The look in her eyes was not the usual expression of disorientation so familiar to arrivals terminals of international airports everywhere; nor was it the look of the world weary globetrotter. Luba was neither disoriented nor world weary; her thoughts were a million miles away, in another place and another time. Her pale, creased face gave no hint of the turmoil that roiled inside her or of the haunting questions that plagued her regarding why she had come and whether or not she should stay.

ARRIVALS TERMINALS are not designed for people with second thoughts about their destination. There is only one way out, and traffic flows exclusively in that direction. Eventually, Luba became awash in the sea of anxious passengers, and she allowed herself to be tugged by the current flowing swiftly toward the automatic doors. In minutes Luba was out of the controlled climate of the terminal and squinting her eyes at the brutal Mediterranean sun.

She didn't even offer a glance at the mass of faces bobbing up and down and waving at every relative, friend, or look-alike who walked through the terminal portals; clearly none of them had come to greet *her*. She trudged on toward the public transportation area to be squeezed — along with six other travel worn passengers —

into a vintage Mercedes that would bring her to Jerusalem.

These sturdy *Sherut* limousines, obviously designed to transport no more than five human beings comfortably, are specially equipped with a row of fold-down seats where the rear passengers' legs would normally go, thereby creating "space" for three more fares. Once all the passengers' luggage has been loaded onto the *Sherut's* roof and lashed down securely, any resemblance between these vehicles and genuine limousines is purely imaginary.

The drivers of this taxi fleet are, by and large, a homogeneous group of frustrated individuals who spend fifteen hours a day behind the wheel. In all fairness, one must admit they are a gracious lot, for they most generously share their frustrations with anyone and everyone who enters their cab, or who finds himself abreast of one of these vehicles at a traffic light.

Almost without exception, the drivers are possessed of delicate psyches, hot temperaments, and a flair for histrionics, notably when it comes to hauling their passengers' suitcases to the roof of their car. (There is a correlation — the arithmetic of which remains a mystery — between the fare and the quantity, dimensions and weight of the luggage accompanying the passenger, but any attempts to negotiate on this subject are generally disregarded.)

On rare occasions amiable drivers surface and expose their passengers to a pleasant greeting to the Holy Land. The effect of their decorum is either enhanced or diminished by the travelers who grace the cab, individuals who may range from polite and cooperative to obnoxious and nerve-wracking, from an eighth-generation Jerusalemite to a Carmelite nun. Fortunate is the passenger whose neighbors are non-assertive, non-communicative, and non-corpulent.

L UBA CZERMAK had no particular interest in the seven travelers with whom she would form a partnership of less than an hour's duration. Had her financial means allowed it, she would have opted for a private cab to the capital instead of sharing one with a handful of strangers. Steeling herself for the unpleasant but relatively brief experience, she strode to the open car door.

"*Bo'i Savta*," a young woman called from inside the vehicle. "Come sit here in the back, *Savta*. You'll be more comfortable."

Savta? Luba halted in mid-stride. *I am no one's grandmother, and certainly not this girl's.* Still, she allowed herself to be guided into the back seat of the *Sherut*. The young woman, already settled into the far corner, had a sweet face, a pleasant voice, and an advanced pregnancy. Luba broke her reverie long enough to return the smile and nod her thanks.

"I to put your bag on top, yes *Savta*?" the curly-haired driver asked, his accent so thick as to make his English almost unintelligible. *Who am I to criticize someone's accent?* Luba chastised herself. *And why is everyone calling me* Savta?

A fair-haired, rather washed-out woman of 40 or so fitted herself alongside Luba and immediately began speaking in an incomprehensible Scandinavian tongue. Each of the others attempted to communicate with her in every language they knew. All told, there were quite a few, but they might have been speaking Venusian. The woman shrugged, sat back, and opened a paperback novel in which she quickly became engrossed. For all the attention she received, she might as well have been invisible.

Luba marveled at the unspoken rule which enabled the three female passengers to be seated separately from the males. Perhaps it was her young companion's prettily tied kerchief, or her own neat *sheitel* that had evoked a sense of religious etiquette among the male contingent; the only one among the men who looked as though the subject might concern him at all was a youthful yeshivah student with a dark luxuriant beard framing his face and a compact *Gemara* cradled in his arms. He sat in the jump seat, making himself as small as possible so as to provide his seatmates with the maximum space. *Modche would have been just like that,* Luba caught herself thinking, and then she tossed her head as if to shake the cobwebs from her mind.

"HAKOL B'SEDER, *Savta?*" the gentleman in the front passenger seat asked solicitously. The yeshivah student, apparently an American, turned in his seat and repeated the question in unaccented English.

"I'm fine, thank you," Luba replied and gathered her cloak of silence around herself once again. She had so much to think about and so little time.

A heavy-set fellow filled the center of the fold-down jump seat, overflowing into the remaining space so that the last traveler to embark had to position himself sideways. Luckily he was young and slender and seemed not at all put out by the obvious inconvenience.

The voluble front seat gentleman took it upon himself to be a sort of ad hoc group leader and Luba's hopes of a quiet ride were dashed instantly. The moment the driver slammed his door, the group leader launched into a detailed auto-biographical sketch. The passengers soon knew more about him than they had ever cared to, and Luba wondered if she too would be expected to reveal her secrets to these perfect strangers.

S O I TOLD THEM, if they want to improve ticket sales and boost tourism, they've got to..." The group leader's voice droned on. "Tell grandma what I said, sonny," he instructed the yeshivah student, and the young man dutifully translated. "His name is Gottlieb and he's a travel agent returning from a tourism convention." Luba nodded politely but her total disinterest was manifest. The boy fell silent.

As the *Sherut* made its way to the airport exit, Gottlieb kept up an animated monologue until the driver called for silence. With its incessant construction and road improvement, the exit from Ben Gurion Airport remains one of the most awful stretches of highway in the country and the driver needed to concentrate on maneuvering his diesel-powered, overloaded behemoth down the nightmarish ramp. The Mercedes, hardly agile with eighteen pieces of luggage strapped on its roof, began to swerve at top speed between car-swallowing ruts and holes big enough to bury a Honda.

When the roadway cleared and the car settled down to a modest 128 k.p.h., the passengers heaved a collective sigh of relief and Gottlieb took this as a sign that he should continue his excursus. Fortunately, he had run out of material. But this, it seemed, did not relieve him of his duties as group leader. He turned to his fellow passengers one by one and urged each to relate his or her own story. Only the Scandinavian tourist was excused, but, since she apparently had no inkling of what was going on, she didn't know that she should be grateful for the reprieve.

The young mother-to-be at Luba's left graciously volunteered to be the next specimen. "My name is Tova," she said in her lilting voice, "and I live in Jerusalem with my husband, who is the principal of a religious girls' school. I've been visiting my sister in New Jersey, but I cut my stay short. You see, this is to be our first child, with God's help, and I wanted to be sure he would be born on holy soil. I went to see my sister's obstetrician and he told me that our child might make his appearance a bit sooner than expected." The smile that lit up her face warmed Luba's heart. Tova translated her little speech into broken

English for Luba's benefit and Luba could almost feel a long-frozen part of her thawing at the young woman's words: *our child... our first child.*

FRAGRANT ORCHARDS of citrus fruits whizzed by the cab windows. The heady scent stirred other memories... a rose garden, a linden-lined boulevard, a perfumed handkerchief, cordite — the smell of death. Again Luba tossed her head. Her eyes met the driver's in the rearview mirror. "*Hakol b'seder, Savta?*" he asked, his brow wrinkled with concern.

"*B'seder,*" she replied, and the others smiled and congratulated her as though she'd delivered her inaugural address instead of merely uttering her first Hebrew word. She felt foolish and, at the same time inordinately proud of herself. When the heavy-set fellow directly in front of her accepted the next turn, Luba found herself surprisingly interested in hearing what he would say.

"Roth's the name," he announced wheezily, "and plastic's the game." This was the yeshivah student's lighthearted translation of his neighbor's somewhat more long-winded speech. There was a brief exchange between Gottlieb and Roth, but the group leader, wary of a potential challenge to his self-proclaimed position, ended the discussion abruptly and turned to the next candidate for dissection.

"When I finished my army service I was accepted at the Hebrew University," the young man explained. "But before beginning my studies, I wanted to see the world, so to speak. The only other country I'd ever visited was Lebanon, and I didn't want to go through life believing that the rest of the world was as awful as Beirut. Some of my friends are living in L.A. — temporarily they all say — and I thought I might join them..."

Four pairs of eyes glared at him. *How did everyone get so involved?* Luba wondered, amazed at the intensity of their reactions. *We were strangers half an hour ago.*

Oblivious to the heightened tension around her, the Scandinavian put away her novel and took out a pair of knitting needles from which a rather revolting sweater front was suspended. Honking car horns and clicking knitting needles were the only sounds heard in the Mercedes for long moments.

"Hey, what's everyone so excited about?" the ex-soldier asked diffidently. "I'm no *yored,* not that it's any of your business. Besides, what if I were? What's it to you? I served my time. Is it so bad to want a little freedom?"

His words too echoed in Luba's mind: *served my time... freedom...*

THE PASSENGERS hurried to make amends. "Okay, okay," the young man backed down, "I didn't mean it. Let me tell you, I had an experience in L.A. that made Beirut look like a *Yom Haatzmaut* party. But that's not why I came back. I came back because this is my home and it always will be. You and I probably don't have much in common, Tova," he said, turning to her, "but I too want my children to be born on

Israeli soil, soil that was consecrated by the blood of my brothers."

Under other circumstances a rousing cheer might have gone up. Instead, everyone simply smiled. Roth patted the boy on the back. "What's your name, son?" he asked.

"Dror," was the reply. "Now, I've had the floor long enough. It's your turn, man."

The yeshivah student knew Dror meant him. He related his commonplace history as briefly as he could: ex-New Yorker, learning in a Jerusalem yeshivah, married with a few small children, etc., etc. Discomfited by the attention of the others, he spoke rapidly and revealed little, then returned his gaze to the open *sefer* in his lap.

Suddenly, the driver slammed on his brakes. Knitting needles, papers, purses and books flew from the passengers' hands. Tova clutched her pregnancy and grimaced. Car horns honked cacophonously on all sides and the driver leaned out his window to inquire about the parentage and physiognomy of the man in the car up ahead that had stopped short without warning.

L UBA WELCOMED the distraction. It was clear that her turn had arrived and she was loath to expose herself as the others so enthusiastically had done. While everyone sorted out his dislodged belongings, Luba sorted out her thoughts.

Why, why have I come here? her inner voice demanded.

Because you have to find him, and this is your only hope.

But you know you're going to be disappointed. You know you'll only end up with a broken heart.

It doesn't matter — you must try!

Why open up old wounds?

The wounds are open and bleeding all the time.

Luba's inner voice was shouting. Self-consciously, she looked around the taxi to see if anyone else had heard.

THE PASSENGERS, having reclaimed their belongings and resettled themselves in their seats, all turned expectantly toward Luba. Even the Scandinavian knitter looked at her with raised eyebrows, nodding her encouragement. *"Nu Savta'le, mah aht omeret?"* Gottlieb probed. No translation was required.

At last, Luba opened her mouth to speak, but the words caught in her throat. Her obvious distress, however, did nothing to deter the passengers; on the contrary, their interest was heightened. Only Tova came to her defense.

"The *Savta* does not have to tell us if she does not want to."

Gottlieb, the group leader, became indignant. A matter of principle was at stake here. "Why shouldn't she tell us? We all told our stories. Does she have something to hide?"

A debate ensued, with half the passengers defending Luba's right to silence and the other half demanding their right to be entertained, as it were. Roth idiotically suggested that if *Savta* refused to cooperate, she could disembark right there on the road. The suggestion was so utterly outrageous that everyone began to shout at once.

The driver had had enough. "Tell her she's entitled to her privacy," he instructed the yeshivah student. "And all of you pipe down or I'll stop the cab and abandon you on the highway! Got it?"

"It's all right," Luba said quietly. "I'm sorry for being difficult and I didn't mean to cause an argument. I just needed to collect my thoughts."

Silence reigned again, but only briefly. Israelis never shirk a discussion.

"Why you come to *Yisrael?*" Gottlieb inquired in pidgin English. "You have got here family, *Savta?*"

"It's odd that you should ask that, Mr. Gottlieb. I'm hoping to find out the answer myself." Luba took a deep breath and closed her eyes for a moment. "I am a Holocaust survivor," she said at last, "and I've come to Israel to attend the Polish survivors' reunion."

THE PASSENGERS looked shamefacedly at one another, realizing now how delicate the matter was and how unfair it had been of them to demand that Luba share her personal story with them. Nowhere else in the world are people so universally sensitive to the pain of Holocaust survivors as they are in Israel. Even the macho Dror cringed at his own thoughtlessness. "Please accept our apologies, *Savta*," he said softly.

"*Kol hakavod,*" Tova congratulated her. "If I were in your position, I don't know if I would have the strength to confront the past."

"You are mistaken Tova," Luba said, her voice more confident now. "It takes far more strength to confront the present and the future with the uncertainty that I have lived with since the war. I spent years searching, but my investigations bore no fruit. Now I must find out, once and for all..." Her voice trailed off.

"Why so grim?" Roth the moron asked. "It will be like a school reunion, all these old *lantsmen* hugging and kissing and talking about old times. Yes, just like a school reunion."

School... It was at the school that she had seen him last. All at once, the floodgates opened up and Luba poured out her story, her eyes fixed on a point in the distant past. The *Sherut* was beginning to make its ascent to Jerusalem, but the driver quickly decelerated when he noticed the traffic backed up all the way to Latrun. Not a single complaint was heard when the cab came to a halt. The passengers were mesmerized by Luba's words.

EARLY IN THE WEEK the SS toured the ghetto where we lived — if one can call the conditions under which we existed 'living.' They paused at the largest school in the area and examined the structure minutely. The next morning the SS-*Hauptscharführer*, a specialist in Jewish affairs, appeared at the *Judenrat* and explained to the terrified community officials that the *Wehrmacht* had many job openings for the unemployed Jews to fill.

"Accordingly, a portion of the ghetto populace would be employed in very heavy labor and the SS would see to it that they were allotted subsistence rations. Those not employable would be denied rations and would consequently have to be transferred.

"'The *Judenrat* need not concern itself with the selection,' the *Hauptscharführer* informed them, for the Germans themselves would decide who would be allowed to live and who would... move further east.

"Every Jew in the ghetto was obliged to be present at the schoolyard at 6 AM the following morning. Absence from the roll call was punishable by execution.

THE NEXT DAY dawned cold and overcast, as though the sun was ashamed to show its face. The air was clammy and still, and a dense fog rose up from freedom and poured through the walls of the ghetto. The sky turned black. Then, without warning, it began to hail, the outraged heavens inflicting terrible damage, with hailstones as big as golfballs pelting the assembled masses. Soon the hail turned to blinding rain, and lightning flashed all around. Thunder followed, booming again and again almost without pause. Bolts of lightning struck the earth closer and closer to where we stood, and with each electrical surge the whole world seemed to leap up. The Nazis, obviously enjoying the augur foreboding their evil intentions, commenced the funeral cortege past the leering *Hauptscharführer,* who stood directly in front of the school. With a flick of his finger he indicated who was to go right, who left; who would live on as a starved slave, and who would not.

"The sight at that line was horrible, worse than anything witnessed in the ghetto until then. The fear that enveloped everyone was palpable as each individual was shrouded in terror. Our only consolation, and it was pathetically small, was that we were together and would meet our end as a family.

"But in their predictably grisly way, the Nazis denied us even this."

THE NEXT SCENE was re-enacted in Luba's mind every day of her life: Modche, her beloved nine-year-old Modche, her first-born child with the rosy cheeks and robust build, was separated from her and sent to the right. She, her husband and daughters were shoved and kicked to the left. Aharon broke away and lunged for his son. He was summarily executed — one rifle shot to the head was all it took and her husband was dead before her very eyes.

Ruchoma and Zlota shrieked and little Leah'le wailed in her arms, but Luba held them all close to muffle their cries. Her own gasp died in her throat.

Zlota, always a sickly child, did not survive the endless wait in the freezing downpour of the schoolyard. Ruchoma could not last six months in the camp. And tiny Leah'le — for her there surely was a special place in Heaven. Of her once happy family, only Luba herself remained. And yet...

"God was my constant companion in Auschwitz. I spoke with him incessantly, and we struck a bargain. I had given up my Aharon and my daughters without complaint; as painful as the loss was, I accepted God's judgment and never once accused Him of unfairness or cruelty. I believed He had taken them in order to spare them suffering, and my faith in Him was unshaken. All I asked in return was that He spare my Modche.

"Since I, who had been sent 'to the left,' survived the horrors of Auschwitz, I was convinced that my son, who, I must assume, benefited from somewhat better conditions wherever it was that he had been sent, also survived somehow."

THE PASSENGERS exchanged a look of pity for Luba. Her confidence, they knew, was ill-placed and naive. How many had lived through the Nazis' slave labor camps? And her Modche had been only a child then.

"*Savta*," the yeshivah student asked, unwittingly adopting the others' affectionate sobriquet for Luba, "did you check with the Red Cross after the war?" He couldn't have known how deeply his question hurt her.

"Of course," she replied, and shook her head from side to side in despair. She had been so certain that God would keep His part of the bargain.

She was *still* certain of it. Modche wasn't a memory like Aharon and the girls were; he was real, he existed; she could even imagine — or so she thought — how he looked today. That he might actually be living somewhere in the world, apart from her and thinking her long dead, was a pain that gnawed continuously at her innards.

"Yes," she repeated, "I searched the Red Cross files. I contacted survivor organizations, spoke to anyone and everyone who might have had a lead, but Modche had simply vanished without a trace, like millions of others of our people who never even became an individual statistic."

B UT WITH ALL of her efforts, the agony did not subside. Luba perfunctorily followed every avenue of investigation, if for no other reason than to convince herself that Modche was no more. Until that was established, she could not go on living a normal life. But this was not to be. Thoughts of Modche loaded into arrows of angst attacked daily. The Rabbis teach that the pain of a relative's passing eventually eases, but there is no relief for a relative who is actually still alive.

Luba was startled from her reverie yet again by the persistent Gottlieb. "*Savta*, you must prepare yourself for disappointment," he said solicitously. The others agreed.

I will never be a savta, Luba thought to herself, but in this Jerusalem-bound taxi, almost from the moment she had landed in Israel, she was a *savta* to all. She felt a sudden burst of warmth for her fellow passengers, even for the foolish Roth who knew no better, and the arrogant Gottlieb who had pried her most private memories from her.

"My children," Luba said at last, "I have told you why I'm here, and I've answered all your questions. I must admit that your inquiries offended me at first, but now I thank you for your interest and concern. May I ask you some questions?"

The passengers nodded in unison.

"Dror," Luba said, addressing the ex-soldier. "That's an interesting name. I've never heard it before. What does it mean?"

Everyone now focused on Dror, although they all knew the answer. "It means freedom," the youth responded with pride.

"Ah, freedom," Luba sighed. "I wonder if you truly know what it means. Only one who has lived under brutes armed with rifles and whips can savor the delicate flavor of freedom.

"True freedom is the ability to share and to give, and even that we were denied. Everything they did was to make us think only about our miserable selves. I, and many others, now know what it means to be free. Let me assure you, freeing oneself is nothing; the trick is in knowing what to do with that freedom.

INDEED," Luba went on, now addressing them all and not only Dror, "you are too young to know the value of freedom. If you have it, you must do everything in your power to retain it.

I have come here to achieve my own freedom, to free myself from an ache that affords me no respite. Of my own free will I have decided to make one final attempt, and at the same time perhaps subject myself to pain greater than what I have suffered all these years."

Luba withdrew a handkerchief from her bag and dabbed at her eyes. "I had three daughters. Leah'le was torn from my arms and turned into an amusing sport for the SS. The Polish crowd cheered in jubilation as she was hurled into the air. Zlota and Ruchoma are also in Heaven with their baby sister.

"But my boy, with his big rosy cheeks and friendly nature, he was only nine and yet it was evident what a man he would become. True, it was more than forty years ago, but I will never forget his disposition. He was quiet, yet warm and generous. He was the most helpful nine-year-old I ever knew, and if I meet a man with that disposition I will have a start."

"But *Savta*," the travel agent broke in, "people change much in four decades. You do not know what has passed in his life: what events, additional tragedies, hardships, that could erase any vestige of kindness."

"Right," Roth contributed, "and even if he is alive, he might not attend the reunion!"

They all glared at him furiously. "*S'tome*, you fool," Dror silenced his seatmate with a jab in the ribs.

Savta tried in vain to fight back the tears.

"Nonetheless," she said in a barely audible voice, "I have to try."

THE TRAFFIC JAM began to break up as if on cue and the driver, usually the most garrulous member aboard an Israeli *Sherut*, remained quiet with his eyes focused ahead on the road and his hands fixed on the wheel at ten-to-two. He was way behind schedule. The limousine was now speeding down the decline to Abu Ghosh, the last descent before the final long ascent up to the holy city.

"*Savta'le*," Tova interjected in her pleasant way, "I for one believe that if your son still lives, he will attend the Survivors' Convention. But what do you plan to do? How will you locate him?"

Savta blushed and then reached down into her oversized tote on the floor between her feet. "I know this is going to sound silly to you," a smile escaping from her embarrassment, "and you'll accuse me of being very 'American.' But I assure you, it wasn't my idea. My neighbors in Philadelphia were insistent and they went out and had this made up."

And with that *Savta* pulled out a T-shirt with a text emblazoned across the front. She showed it first to Tova and a slight giggle escaped the girl's lips. "Well, that's American ingenuity for you," she commented, and passed the shirt to the yeshivah student in front of her. He smiled and handed it on to Roth and Dror.

"Let's see it here," Gottlieb said, rotating in his seat. He put on his reading glasses, an unnecessary gesture since the words were set in poster height, but his spectacles nonetheless added an aura of scholarly professionalism. Obviously Gottlieb would have a remark to share and he wanted it to appear appropriate and well thought out. But before he offered his sagacious opinion, decency compelled him to hold up the T-shirt for the benefit of the driver.

As he spread out the shirt between his hands, he read the text aloud:

I AM LUBA CZERMAK FROM LODZ, LOOKING FOR MY SON MODCHE (MORDECHAI) YISRUEL BORN ON 14 KISLEV 5692

The cab lurched forward and stalled as the driver rammed the brakes to the floorboards. His eyes bulged, his jaw dropped, and a primal scream rent the air.

"Mama!"

Heard from: Students of Bnot Torah Institute

It's a Blast

YESHIVAH LIFE, wherever and whenever, is an amalgam of strange stories, some improbable, some well beyond that. But the stories that will last forever are those that drift back and forth across the border between the mad and the mundane, between bedlam and trivia.

If you grew up with a concept of adventure that did not include run-ins with the Law, collisions with Fate, or volatile science experiments that launched your attic into orbit, you may have difficulty appreciating the madcap escapades of Danny Horowitz. But if, like most normal lads, you had your share of excitement, Danny's story will strike a responsive chord.

Danny Horowitz never looked for trouble; he didn't have to. It sought him out with the accuracy of a heat-sensor missile homing in on a flame-throwing target — and with equally explosive results. From everything I've heard, "bedlam" was Danny's middle name, and that qualifies his story for inscription in the annals of yeshivah lore.

That Danny Horowitz eventually found his way to a safe and productive profession, and one that so serendipitously revolved around his penchant for science, was, perhaps, the most astounding event of his entire life. But in order to understand that, you'd have to know a lot more about Danny Horowitz.

Now, the truth will usually endure a little embellishing, especially for a worthy cause, but in this particular case, there was no need to embellish. I have merely recorded the words of Danny's lifelong friend and admirer, who pledged up and down to their veracity, although in the end, I'll admit that doesn't amount to much of a guarantee.

You see, the source, Leibel Finkelstein, has a reputation for exaggeration and overstatement, a compulsion to rev up the facts. Most associates of Finkelstein consider it S.O.P. to discount 60 or 70 percent of anything he has to say. If Leibel were to tell you, for example, that he was married four times, you could figure it was about a marriage and a half. It isn't a question of deceit. Just the opposite: he wants to spice up the truth, to make it so sharp that you can taste it exactly as he did.

For Leibel Finkelstein, a party to some of the events recounted herein, the facts, I think, were formed by sensation, instead of the other way around. When I listened to his tales of Danny Horowitz, I found myself performing rapid calculations in my head, subtracting superlatives, figuring the square root of an 'absolutely,' and then multiplying by 'maybe.'

Still, I have to hand it to Leibel: no matter how skeptical my gaze or quizzical my eyebrow, he never once backed down. He claimed either to have witnessed every detail of these events with his own eyes or to have heard about them first hand. When I challenged him about the bakery incident, from the fender to the shirt, he protested vehemently, insisting, "I was *there*! I was *there*!"

WHAT he was referring to was the day Danny Horowitz decided to join his classmates who were kashering a local bakery. Under the watchful eye of their yeshivah's principal, Rabbi Nosson Greenfield, fifteen boys rubbed and scrubbed the place until it was surgically clean.

They went over every inch of counter space. Washed down all the bakery racks. Sterilized shelf after shelf, front and back. Sanded down the bench where the bread was made. And scoured the mixers.

The place was almost ready to receive Rabbi Greenfield's stamp of approval when the two bakers who worked the early morning shift arrived. Shorty O'Brien and Vinny DiVito were products of two different cultures, from two different neighborhoods, with two different perspectives on life, but they kneaded well together.

"Not bad," they noted, bobbing their chins in unison. Indeed they were so impressed by the goings-on that they offered to pitch in and help the aching, perspiring boys. The air soon became redolent with the pungent fragrance of sweat and the bakery took on that unique aroma of a basketball locker room after double overtime. With these distinctive fumes wafting about him, Vinny removed his white silk Othello-of-Milan shirt.

"I don't wanna get dis baby dirty. It put me out eighty bucks," he said as he folded it up gingerly.

"Dat's all?" Shorty asked, admiring the high-style designer garment.

"Yeah, I bought it hot," Vinny explained, solving the mystery.

DANNY, as usual, walked in late. And as usual, he didn't come emptyhanded. Sometimes he would have a live rabbit tucked under his arm, at other times an unfathomable science textbook, and frequently an unrecognizable object which his companions knew better than to inquire about. A question demanded an answer, and in Danny's case this meant either a protracted excursus, or a demonstration which always ended up with a *bang*!

On this particular occasion he was carrying a rather badly mangled car fender.

"Dis ain't no spare auto parts warehouse," Shorty O'Brien shouted to the latecomer above the cleaning din.

"Oh, I know that," Danny replied, placing the filthy fender down on the immaculate counter top. "Just a little accident." He smiled sheepishly. "You see, the only way I could avoid the dumpster behind the bakery was by taking a sharp turn into the parking lot. Miraculously there was a parking space right ahead of me, but it wasn't really meant for a vehicle of my car's dimensions. Come to think of it, I wonder if a bicycle would have fit into it. Anyway, I managed to squeeze in somehow, but I noticed that the cars on both sides of me were sort of moving with me, know what I mean? When I drove forward, so did they, and when I reversed, they did too. Aha! I deduced, Our fenders must be engaged."

"*Mazel tov!*" fifteen voices wished as one, but Leibel claimed that the sardonic note was lost on Horowitz.

Undeterred, he continued describing his driving prowess. "I realized that any one of the cars could only leave the parking lot as part of a three-some, and that's probably more than their owners bargained for, not to mention the fact that the street isn't suited to triple parking even if you count the sidewalks. Furthermore, how would I ever find *my* car again, if it were driven off by a different driver in tandem with two others. The drawbacks were endless, so I did some incredible maneuvering to extricate my fender. And there you have it," he concluded, giving his fender a fond pat. "Quite literally, I might add.

"Well, now that I'm here, how can I help?"

"Grab a clean rag and start seasonin' d' pans," Vinny instructed. Stacks of brand-new bread pans and cake tins were piled against the wall. Before they could be used, they had to be well greased and the grease baked in.

D ANNY WALKED OVER to the corner, picked up a sturdy *shmatte* and immersed it in a five-gallon drum of cooking oil. He then carried the dripping cloth across the room, tracking up the floor as he went, and began to work the golden fluid into the iron-gray baking pans that had been collecting dust for weeks.

When this rag had served its purpose and gaping holes appeared in the material, Danny reached for a fresh *shmatte* and accorded it the same honor. In minutes, the formidable remnant bore not a trace of its former pristine whiteness; in fact, it was jet black. By this time Horowitz had really gotten into the swing of it and was applying all of his ample muscle to the chore. He attacked the next pan with vigor.

At this point, Vinny DiVito decided that he had finished his tour of duty and began to look for his shirt.

"Hey! Where is it?"

Shorty perked up. "Where's what?"

"My shirt. My good shirt."

"I dunno. Look around. Nobody baked it."

"I put it in dis corner. So it wun't get rooned."

Some of the yeshivah students eager to re-clothe the gamy Vinny, joined in the search. DiVito's deportment, coupled with the manly aromas he was exuding, imbued them with a sense of urgency. One student thought he was onto something when he spotted the pile of rags in the corner. He sorted through the oil-drenched *shmattes*, examining the effect of grease on dirt until Danny brought him to an abrupt halt.

"There's nothing there," Horowitz called out. "Just filthy rags like this one," and he held up the specimen he was working with.

For a moment that alabaster, niveous chalki-ness, that canescent lactescence, that glistening snowy whiteness of the regal Othello-of-Milan pure silk eighty-smacker shirt reproduced itself in the color of DiVito's astonished face. But only for a moment. In milliseconds it was transformed into deeper and deeper shades of red, going from livid to violent in the blink of an eye. "DAT'S MY SHIRT!!!!!" he screamed, clutching a truncheon-sized rolling pin.

Vinny started sprinting across the bakery, dashing like an deer in hunting season, until he hit the trail of oil Danny had dripped on the floor. Impelled by a five-yard start, accelerated by a lust for vengeance, and fueled by Gold's Cooking Oil, DiVito crashed clangorously into an industrial mixer, the rolling pin clutched tightly in his hand, striking a stunning blow to his somewhat hollow cranium.

Horowitz was quivering with fear. In an involuntary gesture of throwing in the towel, he tossed DiVito's erstwhile shirt at the wounded baker accordioned into the mixer.

Vinny raised himself, removed the rolling pin from the furrow in his skull, and inspected the torn, streaked, greasy silk in his tremulous hands. In a voice one would normally attribute to Attila the Hun, he boomed out stereophonically, "YOU ROONED IT! MURDER-ER-ER!!!"

DiVito reached for the car fender and a quaking Danny Horowitz began to dictate his Last Will and Testament to the yeshivah guys who were standing around like hairy black-and-white trees in a petrified forest. "My set of magic tricks goes to Marty, my sci-fi books go to that freshman who keeps bugging me..."

In the midst of Danny's recitation and Vinny's wind-up before moving in for the kill, all eyes shifted to Shorty O'Brien, who had started laughing maniacally. "De kid killed ye shirt. You should have him arrested! You should have him collared! Get it? HAHAHAHAHAHA. Hey, I got a better idea! Put de cuffs on him! HAHAHAHAHA. *Buttonhole* him, Vinny! HAHAHA."

The boys nervously laughed along, hoping this diversion might effect a reprieve or earn a stay of execution. Vinny obviously wasn't amused, but Shorty couldn't stop laughing. In fact, DiVito was getting madder by the minute. The only reason he didn't go after someone was that he didn't know whom to hit first — the kid, or his partner.

At that critical moment seconds away from a bakery brawl, Rabbi Greenfield interceded. "Don't worry, sir," he said in a conciliatory tone while at the same time keeping well out of range. "The yeshivah, our school, that is, will shoulder the responsibility of reimbursing you for your shirt. As a matter of fact, I'll pay you back right now..."

"*Back?*" Shorty O'Brien repeated, laughing so hard he was in tears. "Yeah, de Rabbi's gonna give you de shirt off his back! And he'll trow in de *shoulders* for nuttin. Just don't go near no oil spills! HAHAHAHAHAHA!"

Vinny lunged at his partner, who by this time was hysterical. "You tryin t' figure my neck size?" Shorty gasped as two meaty hands gripped his throat. "Wait! Get a new shirt! I'll pay for it. I'll pay for it! I saw more hot stuff dis mornin by dat street vendor dan dey got in de mall."

Vinny released his grip and Shorty whipped two crisp fifty-dollar bills out of his wallet.

"It was wort it, believe me," Shorty explained to the Rabbi. "Fer years we been workin side by side. Every day we plays jokes on each odder, but nuttin, *nuttin* ever even came close to dis!"

"Kid," Vinny said to Danny, "you're lucky I'm a nice guy." DiVito slipped his car keys from his pocket and stalked out the door. As all of the boys resumed breathing, Danny ran out after the baker. Something about those car keys and the car make insignia on the chain made him fear that his own vehicle might be parked close, embracingly close, to DiVito's.

TALK ABOUT TROUBLE, and Danny Horowitz's name always came up. If "bedlam" was his middle name, then "trouble" was his *nom de guerre*. Every science classmate of his can attest to that. On one less fortunate occasion than others, he performed a science experiment that nearly ended up destroying the classroom, or so claims Leibel Finkelstein, unofficial Horowitz's High Jinks Historiographer.

This particular incident started out innocently enough. Danny had exhumed the remains of an old Motorola television set from its curbside grave and lugged it laboriously some six blocks to the yeshivah. After denuding it of its cabinet and chassis, Horowitz attached a solar cell to the exposed picture tube for experimental purposes.

Simplicity was never Danny's aim. His presentation was intended to be both dramatic and captivating, not to mention innovative. Nothing pleased him more than to have his classmates sit enraptured before him as he played pedant and engaged in lengthy discourses. And nothing pleased *them* more than to kill a frequently boring hour of Mr. Sharf's science lesson with one of Danny's diversions.

The class found Horowitz's latest prop irresistible, and the teacher agreeably turned over his mantle to the would-be scientist. At first Danny passed his hand over the solar cell and the screen turned dark; then he removed it, and the screen turned light.

"Magic!" the class chimed in unison.

Since the first experiment had been such a success, Danny decided that the time was ripe to teach his classmates the rudiments of circuitry. He plugged in the television and began to explain how electric current travels. At one especially salient juncture, Danny raised his screwdriver, for want of a wooden pointer, for emphasis. Somewhere between describing the reaction to ambient conditions and the dispatch of an analog signal, Danny connected with current events and got the shock of his life.

WHAT HAPPENED NEXT would have been disqualified from *Ripley's Believe It or Not* as outrageously unbelievable. Hundreds of volts surged through Danny's arm, sending him three feet into the air. The screwdriver was released on the upswing and scored a direct hit to the wall clock, which came tumbling down.

This clock was not to have an uneventful journey in its conformance to the law of gravity. It landed (first) on a tall bookcase, dislodging several oversized textbooks. The tomes, in collusion with the clock (or what was left of it), tipped over the gerbil cage, emancipating the rodents in a rather spectacular way.

Leibel Finkelstein took a deep breath before he described what happened next. Mere words, perhaps, cannot do justice to Leibel's superb graphic rendition of a screwdriver in flight, a clock freefalling through a vertical textbook labyrinth, and gerbils excitedly celebrating their manumission. Trust me; it was awe-inspiring.

Books that were still tumbling from the shelf struck by the clock sent the gerbils into a panic. They scurried hither, thither and yon, colliding like furry bumper cars and emitting heart-rending squeaks from their inarticulate little throats. The science teacher, who was preparing to celebrate his wedding anniversary that evening, hadn't bargained on the day's turn of events and had unfortunately placed upon his desk a vase of flowers which he had intended to bring home to his wife.

The vase and its contents were in the direct path of the terror-driven rodents who unwittingly were about to receive their first swimming lesson. Not only did two pints of water and four daisies, two tulips, three carnations, ten roses, five chrysanthemums, seven tiger lilies, six gladioli, eight gardenias, and a wisp of wisteria give the gerbils the most aromatic wash of their lives, it also wreaked havoc on the students' science term papers innocently awaiting their grades. They began to hemorrhage blue and black ink down the front of the desk and all over the floor.

In the meantime, the original culprit (the screwdriver — not Danny Horowitz) shorted the television set, which began to convulse in protest. At first the faces of those seated in front of the TV were lit up in tones of first-degree-burn pink and cobalt-therapy blue. Their technicolor complexions then turned black as smoke belched from the

TV and sparks flew through the air, triggering the schoolroom sprinkler system.

The overcast skies seemed to derive smug satisfaction from the showers deluging the formerly (although briefly) cheerful students in Danny's class. But in fact the action was only just beginning. The sprinkler not only soaked everything and everyone; it also automatically activated the yeshivah's fire alarm and alerted the municipal fire department.

With alarm bells clanging, fire engine klaxons sounding, police car sirens wailing, students yelling, gerbils fleeing, water soaking, flowers floating, books sinking, and the TV stinking, Danny and his classmates made their way out of the science classroom and into the pages of history.

L EIBEL FINKELSTEIN got very animated when he told this part of the story and his cadence quickened. Then he paused to mention that this was all a preamble to one of Danny's more monumental encounters with science.

Leibel explained that Danny really loved science, especially chemistry. Once in a lab, he was truly in his element — only it was one never to be found on the periodic tables. Surrounded by test tubes, beakers and burettes, awash in a sea of chemicals, he could concoct and titrate for hours. Even the TV-sprinkler fiasco could not dampen his craving to experiment.

Compounding this love was an affection for science fiction, although his mother could have rightfully argued it was more of an affliction.

Danny read every author he could get his hands on, from Asimov to Heinlein to Pohl and back again. If a new book came out, Danny was sure to have it. Marty Schmidt, Danny's roommate, was just as devoted to his stereo, his headphones seeming to be a natural outgrowth of his skull. So it wasn't long before the two boys became known as Hi-Fi and Sci-Fi.

I F EVER there was an unusual pair of room- mates in this yeshivah, where in fact everyone was unusual and no one, absolutely *no one*, at least upon entering those hallowed halls, was stereotypically *yeshivish*, Horowitz and Schmidt were they. The two had an insatiable hunger for their hobbies, Horowitz — science, and Schmidt — electronics, much to the dismay of Rabbi Greenfield.

One day, as Danny sat voraciously reading the latest science fiction blockbuster, he emitted a long, low whistle, the kind that Marty knew meant trouble.

"Uh, oh. What's up?" he asked.

"I'm reading an explosive book."

"You mean it's really exciting?"

"No, I mean it explains how to make explosives. It's sort of like an anarchist's cookbook. I can hardly wait to try some of the recipes. They seem a cinch."

"Cinch? What about safe?"

"Don't worry. I'm good at this stuff. When did I ever mess up an experiment?"

Marty eyed his roommate, looking for latent signs of dementia. He then began to reenact the TV episode, his hands simulating scurrying gerbils and sprinkling water. After this he folded his arms across his chest and set his features in an expression that seemed to shout, "Well, what do you have to say about *that*?"

Danny suddenly remembered the solar cell fiasco. "All right, so I do get carried away once in a while," he conceded, "but you have to admit it was a whole lot better than a pop quiz from Mr. Scharf."

WEEKS PASSED and although Marty had forgotten all about Danny's machinations, combustible wood was burning in Horowitz's head as he contemplated his next science project. The result was a refined mix of gun powder and other ignitables sure to provide plenty of bang for the buck. (Un)fortunately, Purim was approaching, and this fact suggested an idea to Danny for how to inaugurate his latest product.

Horowitz's tinkering went virtually unnoticed by his class- and dorm-mates since each was so preoccupied with his own Purim *shtick* and costumes. These matters were of little concern to Danny, and Marty pressed him as to his choice of Purim persona. "You gotta decide, Danny. You need time to get your getup together."

"It's already decided."

"Oh, yeah? Well, what are you going as?"

"A mad scientist!" the mad scientist announced triumphantly.

"For that you have to dress up?!"

"Wait until you see my props!" he replied, and Marty knew enough not to inquire further.

PURIM NIGHT, which also happens to be the night of the yeshivah's Purim *shpiel* — a major event in this yeshivah perhaps better known for its *shpiel* than for its level of learning — there were no absentees. The costumes were as varied as the personalities of their wearers. There were Biblical characters (one student dressed up as all twelve tribes), political characters ("You won't have me to kick around anymore!"), cartoon characters ("T-T-T-That's all folks!") and plain old characters, some resembling neither animal, vegetable or mineral. Then there were the weirdos, like the guy dressed as a CD player ("Guess what I am!" [no one did]), to mention some of the less original getups.

Danny was clad in a lab coat, the pockets of which were bulging with oversized test tubes filled with an unidentified gray powder, that was Danny's own brew. This moonshine contained: 1) white saltpeter, KNO_3, (potassium nitrate) 75%; 2) powdered charcoal, (carbon) 14%; 3) powdered sulfur 10%; 4) several drops of water, H_2O 1%. Protruding from each tube was an extremely long wick which, by Leibel's account, had done previous duty as a gym sneaker shoelace.

After the *shpiel* was over, spirits were high and the boys began to dance and drink with great abandon. Soon they felt it was too stuffy in the school building so they went outside for some sobering fresh air. Shimi Nussbaum, looking as much like Humphrey Bogart as a yeshivah student could, was fooling around with a cigarette lighter. He wore a dirty tan trench coat, a wide-brimmed hat placed rakishly on his crown, and a cigarette dangling from the corner of his mouth.

According to Leibel, Shimi Nussbaum could not be blamed for what happened next. He was already in his cups and the temptation was overwhelming. Thus, without giving it too much thought, or certainly not more than could be expected from him in his condition, Nussbaum took the cigarette lighter and lit one of the wicks sticking out of Horowitz's lab coat. Had he only considered for a moment the kind of ingredients Horowitz was likely to have packed into a test tube, the landscaping around the yeshivah might have retained its original appearance, but that was not to be.

When Danny caught on to what was happening, nanoseconds before it was too late, a seizure of fear overcame him. The powder keg set to detonate in his pocket made Vinny DiVito's grip on Shorty O'Brien's throat seem like hush puppies.

"*Shema Yisrael!*" he shouted, covering his eyes with one hand and tossing the tube as far as he could with the other.

Leibel claims that the test tube exploded just before it hit the ground, but he conceded that there were other witnesses present, admittedly not in full possession of their faculties, who contest this point. In any event, an ear-shattering KABOOOOM!!!!!! was heard, resulting in a scene that would have done Hollywood proud.

The dancing suddenly came to a dead halt and the boys began to flee in two directions: some ran to the sight of the explosion for a better view, and some ran for cover.

"Who did it?"

"What happened?"

"Did you see the flame?"

"Wow! Look at that crater!"

"Where's the meteor?"

Indeed a mighty hole was gouged out of the earth and two nearby trees now collapsed into each other's leafy embrace.

"We kinda thought it looked pretty special," Leibel said later, but apparently Rabbi Greenfield didn't share their opinion. As a matter of fact, he seemed considerably irritated, but that was before he'd surveyed the damage from close up. Once he'd gotten a better look, his face went Othello-of-Milan white.

He thumped his hand against his head several times and then sought out the one he was sure to be the culprit.

"Mr. Horowitz?"

"Reporting, sir."

Rabbi Greenfield stood silent for a moment, at a temporary loss for words. The product of a far more conventional yeshivah, he was accustomed to boys being admonished for raiding the *cholent* pot Friday night, not showing up for *minyan,* and other semi-excusable misdemeanors. These kinds of infractions would have been practically a blessing in this yeshivah.

Nevertheless, nothing that he had seen since taking over the helm of the academy was even in the same stratosphere as what Horowitz had just perpetrated. Danny remained stationary and the other boys crowded around, pleading with their eyes for Rabbi Greenfield not to spoil their Purim fun. For long seconds the two stood there until Rabbi Greenfield finally allowed a twinkle to enter his eyes. "Will you kindly cease and desist any further attempts to alter the yeshivah's architecture or grounds." It was more a prayer than a ·request.

"I'll try."

AND DANNY HOROWITZ did try, until one hot, muggy night in early June. The day Danny was put to the test, and failed, is in part a funny story. Yet to hear Leibel Finkelstein tell it, you'd think it was intended as a straight tragedy. Leibel never once smiled, even as he described Danny's crazy antics. There was a dark, far-off look in his eyes, a kind of existential sadness, as if he were troubled by something hidden beneath the story's surface.

Whenever an audience laughed at Leibel's rendering, he would sigh and wait it out, displaying a modicum of tolerance. The one thing that he couldn't stand, though, was disbelief. He'd always get edgy if someone questioned one of the details.

Leibel would peer down at his hands, silent and thoughtful. After a moment his voice would flatten out. Then he'd tell the audience to listen up.

"You don't believe it?" he would challenge. "Fine with me. But you just don't know how science was a part of Horowitz and how unusual a group of boys it was that made up that yeshivah."

THE HUMIDITY must have been 98%," Leibel said, scanning the sky with his eyes as if the weather report were written there. So hot that even the least studious boys were drawn into the *beis midrash* where there was air conditioning. Since the yeshivah was located on the perimeter of the inner city, it had to contend, all too often, with hostilities from the natives. The frequency of incidents seemed to have a direct correlation to the weather: "hot summer in the city" was often a catalyst for trouble.

On this memorable night, Leibel said, they came en masse, maybe twenty of them, brandishing ice picks, chains, and a cool, blank, doped-up look which was anything but friendly.

They began with the obscenities. The shouts, taunts, curses and foul-mouthed insults were almost unintelligible due to the local dialect, but the general idea was adequately conveyed. Obviously they were looking for a response, a counter-provocation, as it were, indeed any excuse to strike, but the yeshivah boys knew better than to get involved.

The failure to react infuriated the hooligans. Their fearless leader, a man whose head bore a striking resemblance to a bowling ball and had about as much sense, took charge. Rufus "Sly" Brown (everyone knew his nickname, Leibel inserted), menacingly hefted a rock.

"Watch dis!" he boasted and hurled the manganese and iron missile at one of the farthest windows. It crashed through the glass, accompanied by a shower of slivers.

Shimi Nussbaum, who had been watching the developments, concluded that the time had come to react. He tore into the *beis midrash* looking for Hi-Fi and Sci-Fi. "We're under attack!" he yelled. "And it's not a bunch of kids, it's a whole army this time! Marty, do you still have your PA system rigged up?"

"Shh!" Marty silenced him, afraid someone would hear. A few months earlier Marty had assembled a primitive public address system throughout the dormitory, for use in the event of a surprise inspection.

"Good," Shimi said, not bothering to lower his voice. "Get on the horn and tell everyone to man their stations." He turned to Horowitz. "Danny, do you have any more of your bombs?"

"Well, uh, er, kinda. I mean, maybe, but you know what Rabbi Greenfield said to me."

"Are you kidding?" Shimi asked, incredulous. "That was then, and this is now! This is a national disaster, a local calamity, our honor is at stake, the ozone layer is in peril, peace and brotherhood for all is on the line!"

ACCORDING TO LEIBEL, Shimi Nussbaum started waxing profound, spewing nonsense thick and fast. Although he clearly had no idea what he was talking about, he must have known what he was doing, because whatever it was that he said had the desired effect. In seconds Hi-Fi and Sci-Fi were dashing to the dormitory under a hail of rocks and obscenities hurled by Sly and his comrades in arms.

While Shimi Nussbaum was coordinating the counterattack, Rabbi Greenfield was resorting to more conventional means, like calling the police. The city's Finest, however, had more important things on their mind that hot summer night, like finding some cold lemonade and similar matters of vital civic necessity. He might as well have called the Canadian Mounties and waited for them to arrive from the Yukon.

By the time Marty had alerted the boys and told them what to do and where to go, the natives had broadened their attack to encompass breaking car windows and snapping off radio antennas.

Shimi outfitted a battalion of freshmen with baseball bats and wooden screw-on legs from their dorm beds, but they were afraid to go out onto the battlefield. "Time to reconnoiter," he said and climbed up to the roof to get a better perspective of the situation. From that vantage point, he could see that things were deteriorating rapidly. He ordered Danny to let the first barrage fly. Horowitz, however, was still tinkering with the ingredients and wasn't quite ready.

Meanwhile, back on ground zero, Sly was

accessing his rich criminal record for ideas as to how to expand the adventure. It didn't take him long. "Hey, man," he addressed his First Lieutenant. "Whaddaya say we trash de buildin'?"

"Dat's cool," Meathead agreed. "Les go!"

The twenty-man strong committee started sauntering their way over. The lawn between the parking lot and the dormitory began to look like a giant caterpillar as the twenty gentlemen proceeded, bopping up and down with a pumping gait, towards their objective.

TIME WAS RUNNING OUT and Danny was still messing with his concoction. Shimi, always one to turn a disadvantageous situation into an advantageous one, or at least to make it appear like one, ordered, "Don't shoot until you see the whites of their eyes!" The irony of the directive was lost on the terrified students huddled together on the roof.

"Danny," Marty pleaded, "it's now or never. Let 'em have it!"

"Bombs away," Danny called, tossing the first test tube over the ledge. The teeth-rattling BOOM! that resulted heartened and emboldened his classmates and the second test tube was accompanied by a salvo of soda bottles, baseballs and select garbage.

The natives didn't know what hit them. Probably no one else in the world did either, except for Danny Horowitz and some science fiction writer. Meathead suffered a direct hit, and although he was dazed, there was no other noticeable effect.

"Hey, man!" Sly called out to his troops. "Dey got grenades! Les get outa here!" And ten times as fast as they had bopped in, they bopped out. Bombs bursting in air and a barrage of garbage causing a glare, gave proof through the night that the natives could beat a hasty retreat.

"Hurray! We got 'em!" the heroes manning the ramparts rejoiced. "The Guardian of Israel neither slumbers nor sleeps!"

"How could He," asked Marty, "with Danny Horowitz and his firecrackers?"

The boys were exuberant over their victory and immediately began planning a celebration when suddenly the wail of a police siren split the night. "Uh, oh," Danny whispered, knowing whom they would finger as the prime suspect.

"Flush the rest of the stuff down the toilet," Hi-Fi ordered. "You guys didn't see, hear or do a thing. Got it?"

OFFICERS Sullivan and Munisteri arrived at the yeshivah with Rabbi Greenfield at their heels. The two cops just couldn't believe what they were seeing. Fresh craters pockmarked the lawn, making it look as though the moon had come to planet Earth. The acrid and unmistakable odor of gunpowder made tongue and eyes smart.

"Whatcha guys got here," Sergeant Sullivan asked, "a Howitzer?"

"No," an anonymous voice came from the crowd, "a Horowitzer."

The comment was lost on the cops, but as soon as Rabbi Greenfield heard Danny's name, he directed the minions of the law away from the dormitory and into his office. Rabbi Greenfield preferred that the police focus their investigation on the culprits who had started the incident, not on the mad scientist who had finished it.

Later that night, Sly was arrested again, on the grounds of suspicion of attempting to cause bodily harm and property damage, but was eventually released because no one could positively identify him. "Too bad he wasn't arrested on the grounds of the yeshivah," Leibel commented.

Three months later Hi-Fi and Sci-Fi graduated from high school, and Rabbi Greenfield breathed a deep sigh of relief. In fact, Leibel added, Danny wished to stay on in yeshivah, but Rabbi Greenfield gently refused. He suggested that Horowitz spend the coming year at a yeshivah in Israel, in the hope that the boy would benefit from the Rabbinic dictum, "Change your spot, change your lot."

D ANNY THOUGHT this was a great idea and his parents agreed to try it out. He soon discovered, however, that he fit in no better in Israeli yeshivas than he had in American ones. Furthermore, since none of the Israeli yeshivas he tried were equipped with a laboratory or anything even remotely related to one, he was compelled to experiment with a number of items not particularly geared for experimentation.

While this did create a certain sense of popularity for Horowitz among the student body, it was extraordinarily unpopular among the various yeshivah administrations. Accordingly, Danny saw a fair share of Israeli yeshivas during his very first year in Israel.

Somehow, Leibel hastened to point out, Danny managed to survive fourteen months in Israel without any major mishaps or run-ins with mischief. That is, until one *bein hazmanim*, when he was doing a bit of touring in the northern part of the country.

Early one morning in Safed, he met up with some American friends of his who had rented an enormous (by Israeli standards) American car to tour around in. The only automatic-shift cars available from the car rental company were enormous American frigates which tended to draw a great deal of attention on the road.

"Danny, you wanna come tour with us?" In seconds Danny had hopped into the car, never even asking where they were headed. Leibel claimed that the boys actually had no definite plan of what they wanted to see; the idea was just to clock mileage and take in as much as they could.

THE DRIVER had only one sense of direction: north. Thus the boys came closer and closer to the topmost end of Israel, until it appeared that they had encountered the entire Israeli Army, in full combat gear.

"Well, I guess it's time to turn around," one of the boys in the back seat suggested. The driver disagreed, insisting that they go as far as they possibly could, because they'd never have this opportunity again.

"How do you expect to get past the army?" someone asked reasonably. "They've got us out-numbered, after all."

"I've got the solution," Danny offered. He removed his wallet and took out his Social Security card, which he had had made up on gold celluloid, decorated with an American flag and laminated. "This should do it," Danny said confidently.

Everyone in the car was incredulous. How could a Social Security card get six American yeshivah students past the Israeli Army and into Lebanon? "It's simple," Danny said. "Pretend that you speak only English and don't know a word of Hebrew. As soon as they see this car, they'll think we must be some American delegation, and then when they stop us for identification, I'll just flash my card and say, 'United States, Social Security,' in a real official-sounding voice, and we'll be in like Flynn."

Of course the idea was preposterous, Leibel added editorially. But that all fit in with Danny's love of experimentation. You see, it really didn't matter if it was a test tube, a TV set, or an army; if it was an experiment, it intrigued him.

So what do you think happened? Leibel asked. They got to the checkpoint, and a soldier asked for identification. Danny whipped out his laminated Social Security card, souped up with red, white and blue on a shiny gold field, and announced in a very formal voice, "U.S. Social Security."

The unsuspecting soldier snapped to attention and ordered the guards at the checkpoint to let the car through the gate. The boys kept on driving, dissolving into gales of laughter over the prank they had just pulled off.

ONE BOY in the back of the car, however, the same cynic who had doubted Danny's ability to get them across the border and into Lebanon, hit upon a second problem. "I don't know how to break this to you, gentlemen, but we are no longer in Israel. We're not in New York either, for that matter. We are in Lebanon, a hostile country in the midst of a savage civil war. Now, normally when you cross the border of a foreign country, after first verifying that it is friendly, you bring along a passport and a visa to grant yourself entry. Without that, you have entered illegally, as in breaking the law, as in being sent to jail.

"Somehow, I get a feeling that this U.S. Social Security *shtick* just ain't going to work with the *Hizbullah*, or *Amal*, or any of the other booby-trapped welcome wagons which may be dispatched to greet us. As a matter of fact, I have a feeling that U.S. Social Security is no more welcome here than the IDF."

Silence fell over the automobile, a silence which clearly indicated that the prophet of doom had a point. "Well," the driver suggested at last, "we can just head back and cut our northern excursion to scenic Lebanon a little short."

"'Fraid not," the cynic countered. "If we turn around now and the army scrutinizes us, which they inevitably will since we turned around so quickly, we'll certainly be arrested for impersonating a fiction or something."

"So what are we gonna do?" everyone wanted to know.

Danny (as usual, Leibel added) started burning pyrophoric wood again and quickly came up with an idea. He told the driver to pull over to the side of the road where he explained his idea. "FeS, that is, ferrous sulfide, which is found in any rock formation lining the road, together with sodium has an adverse reaction on a battery, and I just happen to have some on me."

The passengers, having either avoided or slept through Chem 101, gawked in incomprehension. "What's sodium?" someone asked.

"It's salt," Danny answered. "When I sprinkle some granules on the car battery it will wage war on the sulfuric acid, i.e., H_2SO_4, present, creating hydrogen sulfide, H_2S, which will catalyze a chemical reaction of white cloud-like fumes and rotten-egg-like stench. It will put the entire Northern Command on alert, but it won't cause any damage. Once the car starts smoking, we can pretend that we had to return to Israel because of mechanical trouble, and they won't hassle us."

"Horowitz was really in high gear now," Leibel explained with sweeping gesticulations. "An alphabet soup was pouring out of his mouth as he spewed chemicalese left and right."

According to Leibel, everyone in the car was duly impressed, except the cynic. After a little while though, even the sober critic mellowed and, stifling a giggle, offered, "If it doesn't work, you'll be arrested for 'salt on battery'."

Danny executed his experiment perfectly, and a major confrontation was averted. The boys sailed across the border without incident. Well, almost.

At the checkpoint, the soldier who had let them through the first time was having second thoughts about his impetuousness. He let them pass but decided to impound Danny's Social Security card to have it checked by security clearance. With significant trepidation, Danny realized that the only thing which stood to be cleared was his presence from the Holy Land.

Horowitz took this as his cue to exit, stage left, and for the first time he began to seriously consider an offer that had been extended to him several times: teaching science to boys in Johannesburg, South Africa. So seriously did he consider it that he was actually on the next South Africa-bound plane. Never did he imagine that teaching high-school boys science could wind up with a compulsory career in the South African Army!

LEIBEL was in a bit of a fix regarding this next incident. There was no way that he could provide first-hand testimony to what had transpired, yet he was insistent, as tenaciously as ever, that every word was true and that the story had been corroborated by eyewitnesses.

The actual incident took place late in the

school year, but it had gotten underway several weeks before that. Danny was teaching chemistry, a subject as enthralling to his students as basket weaving or ballet dancing. To try and capture their interest, he recounted for them how his chemistry had paid off when his high school yeshivah had been under siege.

All of a sudden his students perked up. "Do you mean if we pay attention we can blow up the school?"

"Wow!!"

"Yay!"

"Pleeeeeese, Mr. Horowitz, make us a bomb!" the boys begged.

"Absolutely, n..., well, I don't know..."

"Pleeeeese! We'll be good in class. We'll even do our homework!"

Danny wasn't very strong-willed, Leibel reminded his audience. But he was also painfully aware of how his weak nature had gotten him into trouble so many times in the past. Accordingly, he worked out what he believed to be a safe compromise.

"If you promise to pay attention, we'll build a model rocket as a science project, and we can launch it after school next week."

"Yayyy!!!!!!!!" thirty excited boys shouted in unison.

FOR THE NEXT WEEK Danny was exposed to personalities he hadn't known existed.

The boys were attentive, polite and studious. So he had no recourse; he would have to deliver.

Danny had never built a model rocket before. Of course, he wasn't scared of trying out new and bold ideas, and experimentation was his greatest love, but nonetheless, he was a bit nervous about the amount of improvisation that this project called for. Every aspect would be crude, from the launching pad, to the fuel, to the rocket itself.

The boys couldn't care less. This was the thrill of their lives and they just couldn't wait for lift-off. Every student wished to participate and Danny therefore divided the class into different groups with separate responsibilities. There were lift-off personnel ("You boys count down"), spotters ("You boys follow the flight plan"), and recovery crew ("You boys chase it"). While he didn't know it at the time, he should have added three more groups to take care of damage control, insurance claims, and compensation.

Back at launching pad 13, a tripod was assembled in the school parking lot. Danny waited until the parking lot had emptied out before beginning. When just one car remained, he felt it was safe to proceed. Twenty feet away from the launching pad were several 12-volt batteries attached to the rocket by a series of wires. The best student in the class was given the honor of starting the current which would propel the rocket to the outer limits of the parking lot. Danny brought the excitement to a fevered pitch.

"Ready, lift-off crew?"

Ten eager boys, hoarse from their rehearsals, croaked, "Ready!"

"Ready, spotters?" Ten boys with binoculars, miniature telescopes and opera glasses shouted their preparedness.

"Ready, recovery crew?" Ten boys clad in sneakers and jogging in place, were, unmistakably, ready.

"Okay," Danny instructed his eager young scientists, "let's begin the countdown."

MURPHY'S LAW could really never hold a candle to Danny Horowitz, Leibel Finkelstein remarked matter-of-factly. Murphy only guaranteed that things would go wrong, but it was Danny Horowitz's touch that assured that things would go wrong with a *bang!* Indeed, Leibel added drily, Murphy's Law should be changed to Horowitz's Lament.

"Ten, nine, eight, seven..." In all the excitement, everyone, Danny included, failed to notice the wind whipping up. The launch platform began to shake a little...

"Six, five, four, three..." At the worst possible moment, it began to tip...

"Two, one, ignition!" The circuit was completed and current went surging down the wires, just as the rocket started to fall. Once ignited, the model was no longer pointing up. It was pointing out, parallel to the parking lot.

"Lift-off!" And that it did. At the height of one-and-a-half feet above ground, the model rocket seared across the blacktop at incredible speed. By a queer twist of fate, it was on a collision course with the only car left in the parking lot. The nose cone seemed to lock dead center on the car's gas tank and did not veer in its path.

"Hit the deck!" Danny yelled, one microsecond before the rocket scored a direct hit. There was no doubt that Danny's special recipe had not lost any of its potency over time or space. The explosion immediately generated a fire which enveloped the car in a horrible ball of flames.

Car fragments began to fly through the air and the boys ran for their lives from the raging bonfire. It wasn't long before the sirens started wailing, bringing to mind for Danny similar circumstances of long ago and far away.

MISTER CYRIL DENSIMORE, the school's Headmaster for General Studies and Danny's boss, ran outside to see what was going on. At first he looked merely anxious and concerned. "Is everyone all right?" he snapped at Danny. "Tell me what happened."

But before Danny could answer, the headmaster came to a grim realization: the car burning out of control was none other than his brand-new coupé.

"What have you done? My new car! You—you MURDERERRRR!"

Shorty O'Brien wasn't there to save him this time, but fortunately the police arrived just in time to save themselves from having to deal with attempted homicide. Although Danny's life was spared, Leibel noted, his job wasn't.

"Mr. Horowitz," Densimore fumed, "for endangering the lives of innocent children, consider yourself suspended until we can review the entire situation."

Danny's shoulders slumped and a feeling of despair overwhelmed him.

FOR THE NEXT FEW DAYS Danny barely left his apartment. His day was divided between moping and wondering where to turn next. He eagerly hoped that an opportunity would arise for him to finally make a positive contribution, instead of causing so much destruction.

The knocking on his door, he had no doubts, was not opportunity; the voices on the other side ordered him to open up immediately.

"Who's there?" Danny asked meekly.

"The SADF."

The South African Defense Force was a turn of misfortune even Danny hadn't figured on. According to Leibel, Danny had to think fast and decide between premature AWOL and entering a term of service that would prove exceedingly hard for him to explode his way out of.

The purpose of the visit of the SADF emissaries was not induction. "My name is van Horne," the officer introduced himself, "Sergeant Dwight van Horne. This is Sergeant Shroeder. We'd like to have a word with you regarding this week's event."

FOR THE NEXT two hours, Danny Horowitz was grilled, questioned, interrogated, inquisitioned and made to feel like he was Public Enemy Number One. Had there been a contest of popularity at that moment between Horowitz and the conspirators of the ANC, Danny would have won...just barely. The army investigators went over every detail of the rocket episode, again and again.

When they were convinced that Danny was telling the truth, the whole truth, and nothing but the truth, they did the same.

"Mr. Horowitz," Sergeant van Horne explained methodically, "in order to cause the destruction your homemade missile did, it had to punch through the steel body of a British Land Rover. If it can do that, it should, with a little tweaking, be able to do the same to a tank or an APC. We would like you to develop it for us."

"Me?" asked Danny in total disbelief.

"It's the opportunity of a lifetime. Of course, you understand that in order to pursue such research, you'll have to become a non-com."

"You mean join the army?"

"Naturally. The choice is yours, but if you refuse, you'll be asked to leave the country. It would be too dangerous for us if you and your formula were to fall into the wrong hands."

"How long do I have to decide?" inquired Danny, still not believing what he was hearing.

"You have twenty-four hours to decide..." the sergeant replied, "or forty-eight hours to leave."

Danny spent a very unquiet Shabbos thinking over his present and his future. By Sunday, he was on his way back to Israel. Leibel noted that the irony was mind-boggling: he had left Israel because of the Israeli Army, and was returning because of the South African.

THE DAY AFTER DANNY returned to Israel, he entered a bookstore to purchase some *sefarim*. This would be his attempt number who-knows-what at making it in yeshivah. According to Leibel, Danny's spirits were so depressed that he was not only praying for a solution, he was *willing* it. And there it was, in the bookstore.

It wasn't a glamorous kind of salvation, like a Heavenly Voice calling his name, a miracle unfolding before his eyes, a twinkling star, or Mr. Fortune fortuitously bumping into him. It was just a little sign which hung behind the counter.

> Due to the increase in the cost of materials for ink, caused by the Arab embargo, all items written on parchment have increased in price by 30%.

"What do the Arabs have to do with the ingredients of ink?" Danny asked the man behind the counter.

The salesman replied that ink was made from gall nuts and gum arabic which is produced in Arab countries like Syria, and the Arabs were carefully monitoring the export of their chemical products to ensure that they did not end up in Israel. "We get them, of course," the proprietor continued, "but it means paying extra duties because they have to go through several hands and come from more distant places."

BELLS AND KLAXONS began ringing with urgency in Danny's head. For once they weren't the familiar wail of police sirens but the long-lost sound of his Divine calling. The opportunity to make a contribution.

Danny discovered that ink used for all *parshios*, e.g., *tefillin, mezuzos* and *sifrei Torah*, contains tannic or gallic acid as the active ingredient. This is mixed with ferrous sulfate, FSO_4, which makes the compound black; separately, the two ingredients are clear.

The conventional method of manufacturing ink requires boiling all of the ingredients with gum arabic and then decanting for two weeks.

As Danny began tackling the problem of economical substitutes for these ingredients, he discovered a far more significant problem with the conventional recipe. Since the ink is produced from ferrous or iron sulfate, after a while the ink oxidizes and begins to rust, creating a significant halachic problem. If the ink is no longer black, it is no longer kosher.

Danny put his scientific head to the problem

and came up with a viable solution by adding inert ingredients to the formula which would prevent the oxidation process from occurring.

For once the Danny Horowitz Law which ensures a bang didn't work, but appropriately, it did cause an explosion — an explosion in Jewish observance. From a greasy shirt, to gun powder, to model rockets, Danny ultimately found his place by developing a product that Jews are using and benefiting from worldwide. And, Leibel added with finality, that's the truth!

Heard from: C. D. Sofer

TWO

The Long Way Home

Michigan National Trust had a lot of rich customers, but they all paled alongside Joe Goldsmith, whose assets were vast enough to keep three full-time workers at Michigan National busy full time. The irony was that twenty-five years earlier, Goldsmith had been a penniless young refugee who had washed up on the shores of Lake Erie. His second cousin drip-dried him at his merchandising display workshop, where he acquired a profession that would serve him well in the coming years.

During the Depression, Joe built theater sets for federally-funded arts programs, and after the war, he started constructing homes for GI's returning from "Over There." He then moved on to land developing in suburbia, only to graduate to large-scale condominiums, apartment buildings and luxury homes for the very, very wealthy — a fraternity to which he rightly belonged.

Joe's office was decorated like a Beverly Hills movie set: bow-front consoles, Sheraton legs, Chippendale backs, tufted club chairs, George II armchairs, hand-crafted Eames chairs in calfskin leather, School of Tiffany vases, glazed tiles in a narrow band just under the ceiling cornices, a round Regency table, Wilton-weave carpet, brilliant red Chinese silk wall covering framed by narrow gilded moldings, framed by a broad burnt-umber upholsterer's webbing, framed by more gilded moldings. It made one's eyelids flutter.

This, of course, was but a shadow of the decor of his mansion. Since Dorothy Goldsmith had not been able to decide between Early Colonial, French Renaissance, or Victorian, a separate wing was devoted to each. Decorating wasn't Joe's forte; he devoted his attention to transportation, or more specifically, to two (in case one got dirty) of the most expensive BMW roadsters ever made. Needless to say, the mansion was only for tax shelter purposes and summer vacations. There was also a winter home in Florida, a spring pied-à-terre in New York and a fall retreat in the Poconos.

Over the years Joe Goldsmith not only built

homes and buildings, he also built a reputation as one of the wealthiest members of Temple Beth Ezra. Temple Beth Ezra, or "TBE" as it was affectionately known, was a cross between a country club and a fraternal organization. The Temple was set on a twelve-acre property outside of Detroit. There, in the privacy and security afforded by high stone walls surrounding the site and 24-hour security guards, the families of TBE gathered for the myriad social events that the Goldsmiths and their cronies believed American Jewish life was all about.

The list was impressive. There was the Men's Club, the Bowling League, the Women's Club, the Israeli Folk-dance Club, the pre-school, the kindergarten, the afternoon school, the Midrasha, the youth clubs, and "activity rooms" where boys and girls could hang out and do nothing. TBE had everything but religious services. ("Our members do many other mitzvas," Rabbi Sally Segal was wont to say. "And besides, prayer is such a private matter; we don't feel we have to formalize it through congregational gatherings.")

O F ALL of Joe's innumerable possessions the one he treasured the most was his daughter, Miriam. Miriam, better known as Muffy, was Joe and Dorothy's pride and joy. From her early youth, TBE had been a part of Muffy Goldsmith's life. She attended the Sunday school and the Midrasha. She participated in all the events, the functions and the parties. And she rejected them all.

"I don't want a Bat Mitzvah," she told her

parents, to their stark and utter dismay. "I just want to be left alone."

"That's impossible!" Joe said. "You have to be Bat Mitzvahed. You're Jewish, aren't you?"

"Of course she's Jewish, dear," Dorothy said, trying to calm her husband down. "Rabbi Sally said so."

"What does she know? She doesn't even understand Yiddish!"

"Please, don't start with that. She's a nice person. Didn't she come over when we were having problems with Tante Bella?"

"Well, yes," Joe admitted.

"Remember how she took her in when we went on vacation? She fed her, bathed her, even taught her how to beg for food. Tante Bella never knew how to do that before."

"Your Tante Bella never knew how to do a lot of things. Except lie around the house."

"Don't say that. Just because she wouldn't associate with you, that's no reason to hold a grudge against her. I loved my Tante Bella."

"If you loved her so much, why did you have her put to sleep?"

"What else would you suggest? She could hardly see any more. She kept bumping into the furniture. She was having all sorts of digestive problems. It was the most humane thing I could do."

"Maybe. But I still say you shouldn't have had

the Rabbi say *kaddish.* After all, Tante Bella wasn't a relative."

"Rabbi Sally says she was like a relative."

"Yes, but who ever heard of a Rabbi saying *kaddish* for a dog? For $500 a month, no less!"

"Look, Joe, let's not get into it. I'm sure if Rabbi Sally will talk to Muffy, she'll change her mind about the Bat Mitzvah."

Just then, Muffy walked in. "I heard that. And I won't change my mind. I don't like the Temple. It's full of fakers. And that includes the Rabbis."

"That does it!" Joe yelled. "Every other guy has a daughter who respects her parents and obeys their wishes. I get a rebel! Listen to me. You're going to have a Bat Mitzvah and that's that. You're going to do what Rabbi Samantha says..."

"Sally," Dorothy interjected.

"Sammy?"

"Samantha... Sally, Joe, Rabbi Sally. Rabbi Samantha was the rabbi before Rabbi Sally."

"You're going to do what Rabbi Whatever-her-name says and we're all going to have a nice party. I've already told the landscapers that I want a model of Israel constructed in our backyard. Then I've hired some actors to come as Arabs and give the place a little local color. The caterer and her staff have already agreed to dress up as Israeli soldiers. I got a great deal on an orchestra. They play all the Jewish music — "*Hava Nagila,*" "*Chiri Bim,*" "*Hatikva*"... You're gonna love it."

"You mean *you're* gonna love it. Me? I'm gonna walk out."

MUFFY GOLDSMITH had her Bizarre Mitzvah and it was a memorable affair, as ostentatious events go. The caterers dressed up as members of the Israeli army double-timing all over the battlefield. The waiters ran around looking like pug-nosed Bedouins desperately in search of sand. A giant tent was pitched to house the shuk. Peddlers inside hawked their wares to imaginary customers and avoided the mules allowed to run about within the confines of the tent.

The Bat Mitzvah consultant, whose specialty was theme parties, overlooked nothing. She rented camels from the zoo to give the guests memorable rides, and the camels were especially cooperative in providing the proper ambience and aroma for the affair.

Indeed, only *charedim* were missing as the Goldsmith grounds were turned into an Israel theme park. Rabbi Sally said it was one of the most moving events she'd ever attended. It was also one of the most expensive events she'd ever attended. In fact, for just a few bucks less, Joe could have flown all 450 guests from Detroit to Israel, instead of making Israel come to Detroit.

With such a gala assumption of the responsibilities of Jewish womanhood, perhaps it was no wonder that Muffy's Jewish education came to a halt at the tender age of twelve. It was probably all for the good, for how could the Five Books of

Moses be expected to compete with videos, computer games and Hollywood high life?

ACTUALLY MUFFY didn't succumb to these temptations as completely as her peers did, for she had a hobby and a blossoming career ahead of her. She was the most celebrated art student in Bloomfield Hills High School and was readily accepted to the Rhode Island School of Design.

Along the way her rebellious nature burgeoned as though she had been reincarnated from the Sixties.

"She's as stubborn as you are," Dorothy told Joe after one particularly noisy argument.

"She's worse. If I ever raised my voice to my father the way she raises hers to me, I wouldn't be here to tell you about it! The next thing you know she'll come and tell us that she wants to go to some far-off place."

And the next thing they knew, she did. In an act of Providence she left Rhode Island and announced tonelessly, "I'm tired of learning about art. I want to learn about life."

"Does that mean you're going out to find a job?" Joe asked hopefully.

"No. It means I've joined the Peace Corps. They're sending me to Samoa."

"Some more what, dear?" Dorothy asked politely.

"Samoa is a country in the South Pacific. I'm going there to teach English to the natives."

"You can do that in Detroit!" Joe fumed. "Were you ever downtown? They can't read or write there. That's probably why they overdose!"

"Whaaat?" Dorothy and Muffy asked in unison.

"Because they can't read, they don't know how much of the drugs to take..."

"Darling," Dorothy corrected, before her husband made a bigger fool out of himself in front of his daughter, "there are no instructions printed on those drugs."

"Regardless, she doesn't have to go to some jungle somewhere, or whatever it's called. I'll buy the island and when it's civilized, she can go for a visit."

"You can't buy a country," Dorothy protested.

"Why not?" Joe demanded. "They bought Manhattan and they purchased Louisiana. If they could buy such great real estate for trinkets, I'll get this far-off island for a song."

"You know American history," Muffy scoffed, "like I know the construction business."

"You know something about construction?" Joe asked, all hopes and optimism.

"No, I don't know, and I don't want to know. Nor do you know what you're talking about. I'm leaving, goodbye!"

"You can't be serious!" Joe stammered, looking to Dorothy for support as the front door to the house banged shut.

But Muffy was serious, and so was the Peace

Corps. After several months of training, she was sent to the South Sea Islands, 2,000 miles south of Hawaii and 3,000 miles east of Australia. Or, to put it another way, Samoa was about as far away from the Bloomfield Hills suburb of Detroit as she could get.

M UFFY WAS STATIONED in American Samoa. Its capital, Pago Pago (population 4,000), was an island paradise that nestled under blue skies and was rife with lush tropical forests, majestic mountains and friendly islanders. One good-natured native caught her eye the very first day she met him. His name was Talolo.

He worked, along with 1,000 other employees, processing tuna brought in by the international fishing fleet that operated in the Pacific. As part of her duties, Muffy was assigned to teach the islanders how to read and write, and Talolo was one of her students.

The two were chummy from the outset and thus, when Talolo made a special request, Muffy was happy to oblige. He handed her an old, beat-up looking book and said, "This book has been in my village for many years. Can you help me read it?"

Muffy was surprised to discover the volume to be none other than the Bible. She smiled at the thought of teaching a native Samoan about the story of the Jews. "Are you sure?" she asked.

Talolo was positive. And so they began, "In the beginning..." Talolo proved to be a good student and an even better friend. The two enjoyed exchanging ideas and comparing backgrounds and cultures. Their Bible-reading class became the high point of their days.

Throughout the weeks and months they studied together, Talolo neglected to mention one thing — he was in line to be a *matai*, a chief of his clan. This was a source of embarrassment to him when he compared his Samoan ancestors with the Israelites. After all, the Hebrews knew there was just one Creator, while thousands of years later, a lot of his Samoan brothers still weren't convinced.

EVERY FEW MONTHS, Muffy would send her parents a postcard from Pago Pago. She told them all about her job. She told them about her shack. She told them about the weather, the scenery, the politics. Finally, she told them about Talolo.

"We're going to be married," she wrote at the bottom of a card depicting dark, muscular Asiatic men at a tribal fire dance.

"She's going to do whaaaaat?!" her father raged, beginning what his wife knew to be an apoplectic fit. His wild eyes bulged out of their sockets. His normally ruddy face flared with anger.

"Now dear, remember your heart. I'm sure he's very nice," Dorothy said, trying to remain as calm as her friends were when their children intermarried. "I bet Rabbi Sally…"

"I'm sure he's very nice," Joe mimicked. "He's

also probably very... uh... uh... Polynesian — you know what I mean? How in heaven's name could she decide to marry a native? The guy probably runs around all day in a sombrero."

"Dear, I think you mean a sarong."

"Sarong, sombrero, serape — it's all the same. How in heaven's name can she do this to us? Imagine what the guys will say when I bring some dark-skinned, voodoo-practicing native into the Temple. Boys, I want you to meet my new son-in-law — Tallulah! It sounds like the finale in a concert, 'Ta la la la...'

"'Mr. Tallulah,' they'll say, 'nice to meet you. My, that's a beautiful ring you have in your nose. And that spear, is it hand-made? And tell us about those little shrunken heads you wear around your neck. How did you manage to get that ping pong racket under your lip and the chicken bones in your hair?'

"Can you imagine? She can't be serious. Tell me she's not serious. Tell me I'm dreaming."

B UT JOE'S DREAM proved to be a full-blown nightmare. That night, Joe and Dorothy succeeded in getting their daughter to the Peace Corps phone in Pago Pago. It was a short phone call, but very much to the point. "You get on a plane and get back here now!" roared Muffy's father. Muffy's mother was a bit more diplomatic. "Couldn't you take up painting again or dancing instead?" her mother offered. "Your father and I miss you so much, and we could set you up in your own little garret somewhere in New York or London. Then we could come visit you on weekends. It would be wonderful!"

"I'm sorry, Mom. Talolo and I love each other. We're going to be married in a few weeks by the Island's administrator. I'm sure when you meet Talolo you'll love him as much as I do."

"Love him!" Joe huffed. "I bet he doesn't even know how to play golf or the first thing about the stock market. Love him, my eye! What would we talk about? Sacrifices?"

"You know what Rabbi Sally said about loving all of mankind," Dorothy tried to soothe.

"If you quote that dimwit one more time..." Joe railed. "She'll never have the problem of having a primitive Neanderthal for a son-in-law. And anyways, she was only referring to fellow Jews who maintain our identical beliefs and economic status."

DOROTHY replaced the receiver and began to cry. And although the conversation was over, the story wasn't, thanks to a momentous moment — the moment that Mrs. Goldsmith met, or perhaps better expressed, was overpowered by a thunderous intensity known as Rebbetzin Hecht. The Rebbetzin had heard about the Goldsmiths' predicament through the Jewish grapevine (Dorothy whispered her secret to Ethel who divulged it to Sadie who relayed it to Roberta who told it to Fran — in the presence of her daughter-in-law, who knew Rebbetzin Hecht) and the

Rebbetzin wasted no time in suggesting, in her uniquely diplomatic way, what to do.

"I heard your daughter's about to marry a *sheigetz*," she said with her typical tact. "I'm sure you don't want it, your husband doesn't want it, and the Almighty doesn't want it. So that just leaves your daughter — what's her name?"

"Muffy," Dorothy Goldsmith replied rather meekly.

"Muffy? What kind of a Jewish name is that? In Europe, we didn't know from Muffys. Of course, we didn't know from Pogo Pogo either. Anyhow, you listen to me, not Muffy. You want that your daughter should drop this guy like a hot potato?"

"Well, yes."

"Okay, then the first thing you got to do is start lighting Shabbos candles."

"You must be mistaken. It's my daughter who has to leave her boyfriend, not me. So why do *I* have to light Shabbos candles?"

"Because you're her mother, and the *Zohar* says that a parent can still affect a child, even when they're apart. You go home and start lighting Shabbos candles, and we'll engage in some other sure-fire methods."

THAT FRIDAY NIGHT, Dorothy Goldsmith lit two Shabbos candles, just as Rebbetzin Hecht had ordered. The candlesticks she used had been given to her by her grandmother when she was wed more than thirty years ago. Each solid brass candlestick was contrived of two golden lions supporting the candle-holders. In the warm glow of the candlelight, Dorothy whispered a silent prayer that her daughter come to her senses, preferably before too many people learned what she intended to do.

Weeks passed and Muffy and Talolo were married. Dorothy didn't know exactly how to respond. So she sent her daughter a pair of antique brass candlesticks, identical to the ones she was lighting at home.

Muffy was amused. "She probably expects me to become a *baala busta*, right here in Pago Pago!"

Talolo was amazed. His big eyes grew as round as saucers, as he stared at the brass objects before him. "I've never seen anything so beautiful!"

MUFFY AND TALOLO set up their house in a small village about an hour from Pago Pago. On weekends, they would visit Talolo's family in the coastal town of Viata several kilometers away. In celebration of their first visit, Talolo's family made a feast to honor his new bride.

In an *umu*, a stone oven about four feet around, Talolo's mother made a fire out of coconut shells and sticks. When it began blazing, she added rocks to absorb the heat. Then she threw in several freshly killed chickens, a young pig, about a half-dozen fish, yams and other vegetables. The whole concoction was wrapped in banana leaves, then covered with the hot rocks and another blanket of banana leaves. A few hours later Talolo's mother served her guests dinner on a long plank table, along with generous helpings of melons, mangoes, papayas and coconut milk. The entire community was invited. At the height of the festivities, Talolo's mother arose, walked over to the blushing bride and said a few words in Samoan.

"What did she say?" Muffy whispered to her husband.

"She said, 'You came on an airplane thousands of miles just so you could be Talolo's wife. As a sign of honor and acceptance, I have given you the name "Lupe Lele," which means flying dove.'" Muffy was very touched. She had always hoped for some sign of acceptance, but this was so sudden and sincere that her eyes welled with tears of pride and joy. Yet before Muffy could get used to her name or her mother-in-law, one of Talolo's four brothers stepped up.

Like Talolo, he was about five foot-seven, with a slim muscular build and close-cropped black hair. Unlike Talolo, he wasn't smiling.

Once more, words were spoken in Samoan. By the tone of his voice, however, Muffy knew something was wrong. She hoped she hadn't committed a faux pas in some way. If she had, she hoped Talolo would apologize. Once again, she turned to him for a translation.

"My brother Sosimo has accused me of betraying our heritage. According to him, I am no longer fit to be a *matai*. If I do not forsake you, he will claim his right to my position."

"So give it to him."

"I can't."

"Why not?"

"I have to be dead first."

BACK IN MOTOWN, Dorothy was lighting her Shabbos candles every Friday night without fail. After four weeks, she visited Rebbetzin Hecht with an unencouraging progress report.

"I see we haven't done enough," the Rebbetzin concluded gravely. "Obviously we have to strengthen the dosage. Therefore, in addition to lighting Shabbos candles you must take on another mitzvah. I know — I want you to keep kosher."

"Keep kosher?" Dorothy gasped.

"Sure, it's a cinch. Just throw away all your dishes and buy new ones. What could be simpler?"

"Well, I don't know. My husband is pretty stubborn about certain things and filet mignon is one of them."

"Fill a *minyan*? Tell him that there's plenty of *minyanim* in Oak Park and in Southfield."

"Are you positive keeping kosher will help get our Muffy back?"

"Of course I'm sure. And stop calling her Muffy. You named her Miriam. So that's her name."

That night Dorothy spoke to her husband.

"You know, Joe, I'm tired of the china we have. It's so boring. I'd like to change it."

"Are you serious? That stuff cost $150 a place setting."

"So? I'll find a worthy charity to donate it to."

"You're going to donate fine china to charity? You've got to be kidding! I'll tell you what, why don't we just invite the poor and homeless to have dinner here. It would be messy in the short run but cheaper in the long run."

Dorothy ignored him. "And as long as I'm getting a new set of dishes, I might as well get a new set of pots and pans to go with them."

"Sure, why not. I'm positive the same charity that's going to be serving its guests on fine china would just love a complete set of Le Cruset cookware to go with it! Why, it would be downright shameful to cook and fry in anything else!"

Dorothy did change her dishes. But changing Joe proved to be a lot harder. "Whaddaya mean I can't have veal parmesan?"

"Joe, I told you. I decided to keep kosher..."

"KOSHER!!!" Joe boomed so loudly, waves began crashing on the Great Lakes. "The last time I heard kosher mentioned was when Rabbi Sally proclaimed from the pulpit that California lettuce picked by Mexican migrants was unkosher. She knows from kosher like she knows from Yiddish!"

"Forget Rabbi Sally..."

"A pleasure!"

"It was Rebbetzin Hecht's idea. She assured me it would help us take care of the situation with Mu — I mean, Miriam and Talolo."

"Who are these people Hecht, Miriam, Ti La La. Can't life just go on being normal? Listen here, just give this Rebbetzin a contribution and tell her it's undemocratic to mix religion with the state of affairs. I'm sure she'll appreciate a donation much more than our keeping this kosher stuff."

Joe and Dorothy battled it out till the wee hours of the morning. "How come," Dorothy challenged, "you let me eat macrobiotics and go on the Pritikin Program, and dozens of other exotic diets, and now all of a sudden you're so negative about kosher?"

"Because if you want to eat seaweed, that's your *meshugaas*; keeping kosher means we're all crazy!"

"Saving our daughter is not crazy! I admit I don't know the Rebbetzin very well. And you may be right. She may only be after a contribution. But right now, she's the only one who is even interested in doing something about the situation. So I want to do what she says. We can always change our minds."

"Okay, okay. Only tell her to start working on Muffy and stop making demands on us!"

The Rebbetzin pursued spiritual activities with unmatched fervor. When she peeled potatoes, she recited Psalms; when she went shopping, she recited Psalms. And every syllable was uttered with one intention in mind: that Miriam wish to be wed only to a Jewish husband.

Back in Pago Pago, Lupe Lele (nee Miriam a.k.a. Muffy) and Talolo lived an idyllic, bucolic life. They truly loved each other, and even more important, they liked each other. The days spent together seemed like hours; hours seemed like minutes. Muffy felt happier than she had ever felt before.

The daily reading lessons in the Bible inexplicably provided a spiritual satisfaction which bolstered their relationship. Indeed, the only blot on their picture-perfect existence was Sosimo. Enraged at what he felt was his brother's betrayal, Sosimo pitched a private battle against his brother and his foreign bride.

The first salvo was a dead chicken delivered to their door. Next was a collection of pig bones. Muffy was afraid to ask what these symbols meant, although she really had no doubt as to their intent.

"Can't you do something?" she asked. "I mean, can't you call the police?"

Talolo laughed bitterly. "There's only one thing for me to do."

"What's that?"

"Meet my brother in a fight... to the death."

After several months, Joe was accustomed to kosher food. He even began to brag about his wife's new-found religious zeal. "Yep, she's a real fanatic. If I bring home something that doesn't have one of those funny little marks on it, she does two things. First, she throws it out of the house. Then she throws *me* out of the house!"

At the same time Rebbetzin Hecht was storming the gates of Heaven and cajoling her cronies to join her. Since Muffy still hadn't turned around, Rebbetzin Hecht concluded that it was again time to increase the dosage. The Rebbetzin picked up her phone and after the preliminary social amenities, got down to business.

"Mrs. Goldsmith, I think it's time we take on another mitzvah."

"But Rebbetzin Hecht, we really have been doing all we can. Any more mitzvahs and my husband and I will both be *tzaddiks*."

"That may require a bit more than *additional mitzvos*," Rebbetzin Hecht commented, "but regardless, since we haven't heard good news, we've got more work to do. I'd like your husband to stop working on Shabbos."

"Mrs. Hecht, you're going too far. My husband's work is his life. If he quit working on Shabbos, he would be miserable. Even worse, *I* would be miserable. Please, you have to understand."

"Mrs. Goldsmith, our Sages say that keeping the Sabbath is like keeping the entire Torah. We need that merit to help your daughter. But we have to start one step at a time. Staying home from work on our holy day is that step."

"Could you be the one to tell my husband?"

"Sure — what's to tell?"

That night, Joseph Goldsmith fought with all his might. But even thirty years in construction wars which had filled his soul with confidence, esprit de corps and self-righteousness hadn't prepared him for the power and strength of one Rebbetzin Chaya Liba Hecht. In *mama loshen*, she told him who's who and what's what. She warned him and she scorned him, she yelled and she *kvelled*, she lied ("I'm telling you, it's gonna be easy and you're gonna love it!") and she cried. By the end of the evening, he felt like a quivering mass of jello.

"Look, Rebbetzin, I'll do what you want," he conceded wearily. "But if this doesn't work, I'm going to sue you for anything and everything my lawyers can come up with."

"Don't worry. It will work. I'm willing to bet your fortune on it! And there's just one more thing: Chanukah is coming up, so don't forget to light Chanukah lights. I want Mrs. Goldsmith to send a *menorah* to your daughter — I'm sure it will help."

I N THE LOVELY, picturesque, quaintly beautiful island of Western Samoa, the happy, smiling natives were getting ready for a fight to the death.

Sosimo prepared himself for weeks. Fueled by the mystique of ancient rite and muscles that were honed to perfect condition, he formally announced his challenge. It wasn't his fault that the victim would be his own flesh and blood. That's just the way it was meant to be.

Talolo was much more philosophical about the impending tragedy. It was as if he were resigned to his date with death. One night, he turned to his wife and asked, "What do the Jews say about dying? Is there a place where your spirit goes?"

Muffy didn't know the answer. She strained to find an answer, any kind of answer in the recesses of her memory. The Rabbis in Temple Beth Ezra never talked about it. Wait! She remembered that they explained that Orthodoxy believes in an afterlife; but obviously TBE's Sunday school didn't ascribe much worth to that doctrine.

"What about fate?" Talolo pressed on. "Tell me what the Jews think about fate."

Muffy demurred again. "Look, I honestly don't know. But if you promise to go back with me to the United States, or anywhere away from here, and forget about fighting your brother, we'll find out together."

Talolo remained expressionless, "Even though I could hide from Sosimo, I can't hide from myself. Sosimo and I will fight. And what will be, will be."

TALOLO and Muffy's grass hut was set back from the main road that led into Pago Pago. Usually, they would sit outside and watch the moon chase the clouds across the sky. But that night they remained inside in complete silence, exchanging wordless glances.

Talolo was very nervous. "It's quiet out. Way too quiet." He stepped cautiously outside, and was abruptly brought to a halt. There was a whizzing sound as a spear landed at his feet. Jumping back inside their hut, Talolo warned Muffy, "They've come to get me."

A stifled cry caught in Muffy's throat. Her island paradise wasn't supposed to be like this. She longed to take Talolo and run with him back to her parents in Detroit. There, as nauseating as life was, at least she knew what to expect.

Talolo stepped outside and spoke to the darkness. A few seconds later, she discerned that their tiny hut was surrounded by Samoan tribesmen. Each man carried a spear to match the daggers in his eyes.

Talolo returned to his hut a final time. "What did you say to them?"

"I said that I would leave you and go with them, as long as they promise not to hurt you."

"You can't go. What if they kill you?"

"I have no choice. If I stay, then both of us will die."

"Can't we do something?"

"Yes, I can go with them. And you can ask your God for help."

TALOLO was escorted to Viata by half a dozen tribesmen. No one spoke. There was nothing to say. Talolo knew what to expect. He didn't know how to get out of it. Strangely calm, he made his way on what he was sure would be his final walk through thick walls of wilderness, triple canopied jungle, mountains unfolding into higher mountains, ravines and gorges and fast-moving rivers and waterfalls and exotic butter-flies and steep cliffs and smoky little hamlets and great valleys of bamboo and elephant grass. During the breaks in the bush he glanced down at the six-inch fishing knife at his side that gleamed in the darkness. For years this appurtenance had been used exclusively to gut tuna fish. Now it would be aimed at his own flesh and blood.

At Viata, the men and Talolo walked another half-mile into the jungle to his family's burial ground. When they reached the site, Talolo found more men waiting.

"Where is my brother?" he asked.

"I am here," Sosimo replied.

Talolo could barely see him in the shadows. "Sosimo," Talolo said in a loud voice for everyone to hear, "I ask you not to fight me. You are too young to die. Even though our ancestors did not permit a *matai* to marry out of the tribe, those days are over. It is a new world now."

Sosimo's answer was brief. "You are wrong. You wish to destroy our heritage through your actions; therefore, you are the one who must die!"

Like a leopard Sosimo leaped out of the dark and caught his brother off-guard. Both men fell in the dust and Talolo spotted a long, thin blade in Sosimo's hand. It veered closer and closer to his neck and the sweat pouring into his eyes obstructed his vision. Talolo was surprised at how strong his younger brother had become, surprised and more than a little scared. Sosimo drove his shoulder into his brother's chest, and switched his tactics to try and get enough leverage to thrust the knife into the soft fleshy area between Talolo's ribs.

MUFFY WAS FRANTIC, her nerves were frazzled. She didn't know whether to stay or to run. Talolo's last words were more of a command than a request, but she didn't know how to fulfill them. She had never been taught how to pray, but she couldn't sit idly by as her husband fought for his life.

In a fit of despair, Muffy looked around the hut helplessly and her eyes finally fell upon the worn Bible which had served as their reading workbook. She picked up the frayed pages in her hands. She opened the book and, with tears in her eyes, began reading: "And they said to Moses, was it for want of graves in Egypt that you brought us away to die in the wilderness?"

Muffy put the book down and started to cry. Between tears, she called out, "God, how could this happen? Please help!" Over and over again, she repeated her request.

But the answer she willed did not come. The walls of the tiny hut seemed to converge with the impact of impending tragedy. In desperation, she picked up her Bible again and continued reading. "What have You done to us taking us out of Egypt? Is this not the very thing we told You in Egypt, saying, 'Let us alone that we may serve the Egyptians. For it is better for us to serve the Egyptians than to die in the wilderness'?"

Again Muffy's face was flooded with tears. "Please forgive me God, for finding You, for calling out to You, only in my hour of need. I'll make it up to You, I swear it. Please, I'll do anything. Just save my husband!"

After her pledge, the answer was practically immediate. The next verse read, "Moses said to the people: Have no fear! Stand by and see the salvation which the Lord will work for you today; for the Egyptians whom you see today, you will never see again. The Lord will fight for you, and you shall hold your peace."

Muffy repeated those words over and over again, uttering, muttering, wishing and praying, "Let it be, oh Lord, let it be!" Emotionally spent, she finally fell asleep.

SOSIMO'S KNIFE was only inches from Talolo's heart. As it crept closer in their wrestling, Talolo realized that he could no longer remain on the defensive. He must attack. Talolo worked his left arm opposite his brother's right and grabbed his wrist so that his brother's knife was, for the moment, blocked. Then he moved his head closer to his brother's and bit Sosimo's ear.

"Yeowww!" Sosimo screamed.

Talolo used this instant of surprise to flip his brother over. Now Talolo was on top. Still holding onto Sosimo's wrist, he started slamming it against a rock. He rammed it incessantly, pulverizing Sosimo's knuckles on the jagged stone.

Talolo could feel warm blood flowing down his hand, but he was not out of danger. Sosimo was using his free hand to poke at Talolo's eyes. Talolo averted him like a cobra dodging a mongoose.

Sosimo tried desperately to gain the advantage; Talolo was equally determined to prevent him. Eventually, Sosimo's grip gave way and the knife slipped from his battered fingers. Talolo flung it deep into the night. Sosimo renewed his attack with ferocity, trying to secure Talolo's knife. He clawed both hands with an iron grasp around Talolo's wrist and began forcing the silver blade towards Talolo's throat. Every second it seemed to inch closer.

Talolo was tired, aching to be free of the tribal struggle that raged within him and without. But he knew that to rest was to die. With his free hand, he pushed against Sosimo's forehead, bending his brother's neck back. Talolo had the advantage now and Sosimo knew it.

In a swift movement, Talolo maneuvered the knife up to Sosimo's neck. With one quick slice it would be over.

"Kill me!" his brother hissed. "It is your right."

Talolo looked into his brother's bulging eyes. "By your bravery you deserve to be a *matai*. By my cowardice, I do not," and with that he threw his knife into the jungle.

Both men deliberately disentangled themselves from each other's grasp. Each was heaving violently. Each mistrusted the other.

"You know what this means," Sosimo said, gasping for breath.

"Yes," Talolo replied. "You are the new *matai.*"

IT TOOK TALOLO several hours to shuffle back to Pago Pago. At the outskirts of the city he realized that his strength was sapped and to trudge just one more step might be fatal. Thus he collapsed on the spot and awoke several hours later.

Talolo's loving wife was worried sick about his fate. When she saw him finally stagger up the steps, she wasn't sure if it was Talolo or his ghost. Perhaps Talolo also wasn't certain, but Muffy clarified matters by crying, "You're alive, thank God, you're alive!"

The next eight days Talolo spent resting and recovering, but by the fifth day he felt up to resuming their Bible readings. By this time, however, they both felt that their book was no longer an English primer. After rereading the verses which Muffy had recited they understood that they had been saved by a Force much higher than themselves.

One week later, Talolo announced, "Now that I am well we must prepare to leave Samoa for good."

"To where?"

"I simply don't know, but we must get ready."

As they prepared themselves for their departure they no longer looked at Pago Pago as Paradise, but as a rest stop on their way to... where, they did not know.

Muffy assumed that Talolo would find a job on a fishing vessel working out of Japan or perhaps Singapore. She was certain that they would either end up in the Far East or join the 20,000 other Samoans living on Hawaii. But she was off by a hemisphere.

O NE DAY, out of the blue (sea or sky, by which overseas mail is delivered), Muffy received a package from her mother.

"What is it?" Talolo asked, holding it upside down and inspecting it from all angles.

"It's a Chanukah *menorah*. We are supposed to light Chanukah candles to remember, I think, the victory of the Jews over the Greeks."

Muffy explained the story of Chanukah to the best of her recollection, and Talolo was duly impressed. He saw personal analogy in the victory of light over might and felt that commemoration by lighting candles was especially fitting.

With no intention of waxing profound, Talolo declared, "This *menorah* is not just a gift from your parents; it is a sign from Above."

"A sign?" Muffy asked, not following her husband's drift.

"Yes, here is the sign I've been waiting for. Now we know where we're headed."

Muffy begged Talolo to explain himself.

"Do you remember the verses you came across the night of my battle?"

"I'll never forget them."

"Of how the Lord effected miracles to lead the Jews out of Egypt in order to bring them to their homeland?"

"Yes, yes," Muffy said, nodding her head, "but how did you see all of this in the *menorah*?"

"Just look: all the branches stem from the source. Now do you see? It's time to go home."

Author's note: They did, and they have children enrolled in yeshivah, a source of tremendous pride for their now fully observant grandparents — on their mother's side, that is.

Heard from: Rabbi Zev Kraines

Crossing the Bridge

THE DOCTORS' PROGNOSIS, pronounced with medical authoritativeness and precision, was unequivocal. In fact, they only allowed a two-day margin for error. Considering not inconsequential factors such as human error and medical breakthroughs, not to mention Divine intervention, two days smacked awfully of arrogance. Yet the grim verdict, worded in medicalese and couched in adjectives like "inevitable" and "metastatic," was stated with the utmost finality: "She has another eight, *maybe* ten, days to live."

Chedva Silberfarb, the patient, was not swayed by the doctors' self-assurance and refused to accept her death sentence. This was not what is commonly known as "denial"; nor was it merely the result of natural human survival instincts. Chedva possessed a profound sense of mission which impelled her to forge on. Not for eight days, or even for ten, but for as long as it would take to achieve her lofty goal.

Throughout this time, Chedva always claimed that she wanted to live — at any price, but little did people realize how sincere was her desire to earn every additional second that she was granted. She strove to live, live in the rich sense that the Psalmist propounds: *Who is the man that desires life, and loves a long life of happiness? Guard your tongue from evil, and your lips from speaking falsehood.* And it was only fitting that she who brought "life" to so many, was awarded extra time for her own life.

If there was one dominant theme in the stirring talks of Chedva Silberfarb, it was the balance in nature referred to as *middah k'neged middah.* Chedva understood that she was living on borrowed time, and like any borrower, she had to make regular payments on her loan or it would be called in. Every second, therefore, had to count; not a moment could be wasted. Obviously her perception was right on the mark, for although the clock was ticking all the time, it did not strike midnight for her for *two full years.*

Such a story, the courageous struggle to be worthy of survival, is best told by the protagonist herself. Prose, as faithful as the transcription may be, fails to convey the fire and sense of urgency of her message, her strident and importunate appeal to improve and repent before it is too late.

IT WAS A tempestuous storm..." This is how Chedva often began her *shiur* and it was not uncommon for her to seem to be talking to herself as much as to her audience. "...and the wind howled, heaving the flimsy bridge to and fro. High above the churning waters stood a terrified woman, clutching the rail for dear life. All she wanted, her solitary wish, was to traverse the narrow bridge to her home. But now, as the storm's fury peaked and the wind's velocity increased, the frightened woman realized that beyond all doubt, in seconds nature would have its way and she would plunge to her death in the raging, icy waters below. In desperation she began to offer every spiritual commitment imaginable. 'I shall refrain from *lashon hara!*' she vowed. 'I will never get angry again, I shall extend myself for *chessed*, I will pray with fervor...'

"After pledging to pursue a life of piety and spiritual endeavor, she felt secure enough to continue to make her way across the swaying bridge. With each precarious step, the storm subsided more, until it dissipated into a gentle breeze.

"Instead of feeling relieved, however, the woman was overwhelmed with consternation. 'How could I have made such foolish commitments?'

she reproached herself. 'Everyone engages in *lashon hara*. How can I be expected to contain my anger when so many things upset me? It is unrealistic for me to devote my energy to others when I do not even have enough time for myself. And if I had enough time, I would pray, but surely not with such concentration.'

"In a few brief seconds, the woman had released herself from every obligation. At that very moment, however, the storm began to rear its ugly head yet again and a mighty gust heaved her against the railing of the bridge. Quivering with fear and trembling with remorse, she turned her face heavenward and declared, 'Oh God, I was only joking! I take my pledges seriously. I will even increase my commitments! Dear Lord, let me just return home safely!'

"We often find ourselves in situations like this," Chedva explained. "During childbirth, in hard times, on the *Yamim Nora'im*, we too feel as though we are crossing a narrow, teetering bridge, and we will pledge anything in return for safe passage.

"Inevitably, however, once the difficult times are over, we swiftly forget every one of our commitments. Is this woman not you? I know in my heart of hearts that she is *me*.

MY FRIENDS, you all know me; my story is no secret." Chedva was addressing her former classmates in Jerusalem several years after they had graduated from Bais Yaakov Seminary. Ostensibly, they had gathered to hear a *shiur* from their illustrious colleague, but in truth they longed to hear what Chedva wanted from them, to find out what they could do to help their dying friend.

"I grew up with you and we attended school together here. I was a student like everyone else, and afterwards a dormitory counselor, just as some of you were. I got married — most of you were at my wedding — and I was blessed with three children and a good job, thank God; I was lacking nothing, nothing at all. Everything was fine.

"Then, three months after my third child was born, I started feeling ill and a terrible weakness overcame me. I didn't know what could possibly be wrong. After all, many women with many more children manage without feeling so exhausted. My arms began to ache, but I concluded that since I spent most of the day carrying the baby, it was only natural. I was also coughing a lot, but it was winter so I didn't pay much attention to that, either. That is, until one Friday.

"I had completed all my Shabbos preparations in advance so that I could see a doctor Friday morning. With no intention of undergoing a checkup, I figured I would merely ask my physician to prescribe some vitamins. At most, I thought, she'll suspect anemia and recommend a blood test. But instead she became concerned over my constant coughing and ordered a chest X-ray.

"As soon as the technician examined my X-ray she reacted as if *her* life were in danger. 'Are you crazy?' she spluttered uncontrollably. 'What are you doing walking around? You belong in a hospital — now!'

"Before I knew what hit me, they were whisking me off to the Emergency Room. 'But I have a nursing baby at home!' I cried, a protest which fell on the deaf ears of the attendants who were already busily preparing to drain my lungs."

By this time, the audience had grasped how ill Chedva really was. Although she hadn't specified the nature of her illness, there was little doubt in anyone's mind as to its inevitable consequences.

I WENT to America for radiation treatments and chemotherapy," Chedva continued. "It was Purim — for them, that is. For me it was torture; I could barely speak. After a brief examination, the doctor said that I needed a blood transfusion and had to be hospitalized immediately. I began to weep; I just couldn't control myself. 'I don't want to stay in the hospital!' I sobbed.

"I didn't know what was happening to me, what they wanted from me. 'I have three babies in Israel,' I whimpered, crying like a baby myself, 'and I want to return to them.' The doctor urged me to regain my composure.

"Nothing could be done, he explained, without my being admitted to a hospital, and I should prepare myself for a painful and protracted treatment.

"Of course he couldn't help," Chedva editorialized. "Only the Healer of All Flesh could, and did. I underwent two chemotherapy treatments in

America and I was to undergo another eight in Israel at Tel Hashomer Hospital.

"After the first three I returned home, but I once again felt ill and my lungs filled with water. I ran to my doctor, only to discover that he was doing Reserve Duty, so I called my doctor in America, but he was on vacation.

"Depressed and frustrated beyond description, I felt myself bracing for support on that narrow bridge in the grip of the storm. 'Master of the Universe,' I cried out, 'You are the Doctor of all humanity and You are always here! It does not matter to You if we suffer from a slight ailment or a major disease, You can heal all!' And of course, God helped.

THE WEEK before Rosh Hashanah, I was racked with pain again and delirious with fever. I trembled at the thought of being confined to bed on *Yom Hadin*, but thank God, my condition improved.

"I managed to finish all the cooking and even to invite guests, just as I had every other year, but I felt terribly unprepared for the holiday season. I was aching to attend a *shiur*, a *shmuess* — anything that would put me in the proper mood.

"Fortunately, a talk was being given not far from my home, but still I arrived very late. I dragged myself in at the very end, just as the speaker was relating a personal story about his *tzaros*. Old, frail and very ill, he had gone to see the Steipler *zt"l* for a blessing. But instead of a blessing, or even a few words of compassion, the

Steipler had bellowed, 'You need a *zechus!*' meaning that nothing else would help.

"I was unable to sleep that night, for the Steipler's wise words kept ringing in my ears. I, too, needed salvation but had no *zechus*. As never before, I realized the truth of the Talmudic dictum that one should be careful to pray before one becomes ill, for once one's health is failing one must provide a *zechus*. My plight conformed precisely to the one described in the *Gemara*. I was like the man who was sentenced to death and my only hope lay in finding advocates powerful enough to stay the execution."

Perhaps others would have failed to see the analogy, but not Chedva. She refused to ignore what she had heard and gratefully and graciously accepted the challenge Providence had placed in her path. "Just as a healthy person has his particular duty," Chedva often said, "an unhealthy person has his."

"From then on, I felt the narrow bridge pitch violently and the tempestuous waters below churn menacingly. I was certain that I had to immediately create a *zechus* before it was too late."

*Z*ECHUS was a familiar concept for Chedva. Years earlier she had realized that in order to receive, you must give. When she had been appointed to the prestigious position of *madrichah* for the Americans in the Bais Yaakov Jerusalem program, she had convinced her fellow counselor to join her in a *chessed* project. "If we engage in this *chessed*," she had reasoned, "we can find a *zechus* to explain why only we were selected for this job. Otherwise we may actually delude ourselves into thinking we deserved it."

Six years later, the *zechus* was to be of infinitely greater proportions. "I searched my soul, trying to think of what merit I could offer God. I wanted to live at any cost, but I knew not how to proceed. For all my will power and determination, I had no physical strength.

"Oh Lord, how I had no strength! I took my three children with me and traveled to all the holy sites in Israel to pray. It was a pathetic scene: a sick woman with three babies in her arms, running from grave to grave. When I returned home I thought I would collapse for good."

But even that did not stop Chedva. She was driven to offer a major merit to the Almighty, no matter what.

PRACTICAL considerations, however, foiled my every idea," Chedva said. "With no energy, I found that even the simplest chores were major hurdles for me. Significant *chessed* projects also seemed out of the question, for my first priority was my own family, who had been neglected ever since the onset of my illness.

"Without stamina and certainly without money, I was baffled and irritated, and time was running out. Not knowing where to turn I opened my *Tehillim*, and the answer practically jumped off the well-worn page: 'Come, children, listen to me,' proclaims King David, and are we not God's children? 'I will teach you how to revere the Lord. Who is the man that desires life, and loves a long life of happiness? *Guard your tongue from evil, and your lips from speaking falsehood.*'

"It was so obvious! Advice that required neither strength, nor time, nor money, and involved the most important of all attributes: fear of Heaven. A guarantee of life in this world and the next, all for just guarding your tongue!"

Something else had fortified Chedva's resolve to launch her campaign. Late one night, in the throes of pain, she prepared to write her will. Rich only in spiritual terms, she had no material legacy to bequeath. Suddenly a morose thought obsessed her.

She envisioned her motherless children wandering from relative to relative, without that sense of security so vital in one's youth, and without any place they could call their own. Inevitably, her children would speak ill of their hosts and kin, who were only trying to act as surrogate mothers. In a flash, Chedva's will was written; she had nothing more to say to her children than God had to His in Psalms: 'Come, children, listen to me; I will teach you how to revere the Lord. Who is the man that desires life, and loves a long life of happiness? *Guard your tongue from evil, and your lips from speaking falsehood.*'

"My children," she cried, "I want you to live! I don't want you — or anyone — to ever experience what I am suffering." With that she seized her pen and scratched out the heading at the top of the paper, changing *tzava'ah* to *tzav hachaim*. It would be a *living* will, as incumbent upon her to fulfill as upon her heirs.

From that moment on, every ounce of Chedva's dwindling energy was devoted to promoting *shemiras halashon.* Not a single day passed without Chedva addressing at least one group of avid listeners on the perils of *lashon hara.*

WHEN SHE RETURNED home from America after exhibiting some initial signs of improvement, she found her house bedecked with flowers and stocked with cakes. The garden-bakery atmosphere, however, did not bring her cheer. As appreciative as she was, she would not be distracted from her mission. "I don't need flowers or cakes," she announced. "I need a *lashon hara*-free environment!" From the day she landed, her phone rang off the hook with friends, relatives, teachers, and assorted well-wishers asking what they could do to help. Her response to one and all: "Simply refrain from speaking *lashon hara.*"

Unfortunately her homecoming was unexpectedly brief. Only days after she returned, her doctor informed her that her condition was very grave and she had to go back to New York to resume treatments immediately. Chedva was crushed.

"I don't want treatments!" she declared in no uncertain terms, her voice cracking. She viewed her medical setback as a personal failure, but this only served to intensify her resolve to touch and teach every Jew to refrain from *lashon hara.*

Before going abroad, she had the unpleasant

duty of parting yet again from her beloved children. "As I was putting my son to bed, I whispered to him that his father and I would be returning to America.

"My little boy began to cry and protest with all his might. 'I don't want you to go! You're not sick anymore! You don't need all those tubes and contraptions!' Then he said, 'I don't want to be left alone. I don't want to be without my Abba and Imma. I'm frightened.'

"'And I'm *not*?' I thought. 'In a city of eight million people am I not also all alone?' Fighting back the tears, I told my precious boy, 'Luzerke, you are not alone. Our Abba in Heaven is looking after you, Luzerke. You are not alone. Hashem will watch over you and He will watch over me as well. We have such a good and compassionate Father in Heaven. You have nothing to fear. Let us say *Shema Yisrael* and *Shomer Yisrael* together. Trust in our Abba in Heaven for He will guard over us.'"

WITH RENEWED faith in her "Abba," Chedva left once again for New York. Before, during, and after her treatments, she pursued her mission singlemindedly. She traveled across Jewish America and Canada and the length and breadth of Israel, going from school to school, auditorium to auditorium, *shul* to *shul*, and house to house. Chedva delivered 75 talks per month, with two or three every day.

Her schedule was staggering — taxing enough to thoroughly exhaust a healthy individual, but she claimed that it gave her strength. Night after night, Chedva would stand up before a group of women, look them in the eye and pronounce, "Refraining from *lashon hara* requires no financial outlay, and no expenditure of time or energy. On the contrary, my very presence here tonight attests to the fact that such a commitment *adds* strength and lengthens your lifetime. And I assure you, the rewards are not only in this world."

Her friends and relatives, seeing how wan and weak she had become, tried to curtail her busy lecture schedule but their efforts were in vain. "Believe me," Chedva told them, "I'm doing it for myself. If the merit of what I am accomplishing will help me, then it is surely better than rest, and if it won't help me now, then it is *tzeidah laderech...*"

As improbable as it sounds, Chedva somehow managed to squeeze her therapy in between talks. Radiation exposure is not exactly a good preparation for air travel, but regardless, day in and day out, Chedva would head directly from the hospital to the airport.

ONE DAY Chedva's chemotherapy was scheduled for 9:00 AM and two hours later she was to lecture in Brooklyn. Her attendants were incredulous. They had long since learned not to challenge the wisdom of Chedva's running around without allowing herself time to recuperate; they had also given up trying to persuade her to postpone a talk when she was suffering excruciating pain. But this time, sheer practicality mandated that an 11:00 speaking engagement was simply out of the question. After all, one never knew how long the wait for treatment would be, nor how long the session would last. And even if everything went smoothly, the trip from the hospital in Manhattan to the Boro Park section of Brooklyn was an hour's journey at best.

But Chedva was incorrigible. "When there's a good cause, God helps out," she assured them, and sure enough she arrived on time. Even more miraculously, fifty minutes after a treatment she delivered a talk as powerful, as impressive, and as searing as any of her others. That morning in Brooklyn, like every other time she spoke, she had little difficulty injecting the personal element: "For my sake, for my health, please don't speak *lashon hara*! Make a commitment to abstain from *lashon hara* for one hour each day. Just one hour! Increase my number of celestial advocates!"

Who could refuse? Who could refuse a sick young woman fighting for her life and asking that you contribute only an hour a day of spiritual bliss that would ensure a better life both in this world and in the World to Come?

CHEDVA'S devotees were given an opportunity to challenge their mentor's "good cause" theory on *erev Shavuos*, when she was given a brief leave of absence from the hospital. Naturally she was anxious to fly home to spend the holiday with her family in Israel.

As soon as word got out that Chedva would be leaving the States, London was on the line, asking if she could stop over to deliver a talk. But even with her kind disposition and unshakeable sense of mission, Chedva knew in her heart of hearts that her time was limited and every moment with her children was precious. She had to refuse.

Her Divine Travel Agent, however, was not content that her *zechus* be confined to North America and Israel. He therefore arranged a major *aliyah l'regel*, resulting in no available seats New York—Tel Aviv. The only available flight was via London.

At 7:00 PM, even as her plane was to depart from Kennedy Airport, Chedva was still being examined by her physician. Needless to say, the flight was delayed and Chedva arrived in time to deliver four talks on Shabbos in London (at four different venues, all of which she walked to unaided).

BACK IN Israel, a quiet revolution was underway. Every Friday evening after candle lighting, as the holiness and blessing of Shabbos filled their homes, elementary school girls were attending *shemiras halashon* groups designed to protect this aura from being squandered on frivolous chatter. There may still be a few isolated girls who do not attend "*Shomrot*" every Friday night, but you can be sure that those who do, won't talk about them.

One day an innocuous sign was posted in a Jerusalem neighborhood announcing an ambitious self-study program for the authoritative volume detailing the laws of *shemiras halashon*, *Sefer Chafetz Chaim*, complete with monthly exams and incentive awards. This novel and emboldening idea was conceived well before Chedva Silberfarb became a household name, but once she began her campaign, enrollment burgeoned from ten to two hundred. Overall, the interest and concern Chedva catalyzed for *shemiras halashon* increased at about the same 2,000% rate.

How did she generate such incredible results? Her appeal was like none other. Young, remarkably full of vigor and charisma, she was unthreatening but irresistible. Listen to her style:

A LITTLE BOY was playing on the dock when a man came up to him and asked, 'Why are you playing here all by yourself? Why aren't you with the other children on the beach?'

"The boy explained that he liked to watch the great ships sail by. 'When they pass me, I wave to the captain with my flag.'

"'You are so silly!' intoned the voice of reason. 'Do you really believe that the captain of such a huge vessel can see a little boy like you?'

"'But he *can* see me,' the boy protested. 'We have a special signal. When I wave my flag, he waves back.'

"The exasperated man was losing patience. 'Stop fooling yourself!' he insisted.

"'I am not fooling myself,' the boy countered. 'I am certain! I know that the Captain sees me because he is my father, and every time I wave, he waves right back at me. A father always sees his son.'

"'*Banai ahuvai*,' my beloved children," Chedva quoted from *Tanna D'vei Eliyahu*, "God will always wave back at us provided that we love and respect one another."

Chedva would then offer practical suggestions for how to strengthen that love and respect, along with a plethora of stories that never failed to strike a chord in the hearts of her audiences.

D O YOU KNOW how important it is," Chedva would ask, "to smile at others and greet your neighbors warmly? I'll let you in on a little secret. I've always wanted to open a *gemach*, but I fear I lack the requisite organizational skills and means.

"There is, however, one type of *gemach* which all of us are capable of running: a smile *gemach*. You can open this *gemach* first thing in the morning and keep it operating all day. And when you're ready to diversify, you can stock compliments as well.

"Even if your compliment may not be 100% accurate and you may, God forbid, be guilty of dishonesty, fret not: we have all been enjoined to judge others favorably, and I hasten to remind you that this is a *din*, not merely a virtue.

"Furthermore, any compliment is an excellent source of motivation. If you commend someone on her clean house, for example, even if it is not so tidy, she will certainly strive to be deserving of praise in the future, and ultimately your compliment will prove to be true."

Among Chedva's incomparable oratorical skills was her exceptional ability to draw her listeners into the subject, making them feel as if they were active participants in the lecture:

"If you allow children to draw whatever they wish, provided that they include a red triangle in their picture, what do you think they will draw?

"Yes, you all guessed correctly. Most children will draw a house with a triangular red roof. Some will surround it with flowers, others will draw adjoining houses, but all will attempt to conceal the red triangle in the artwork.

"Adults do the same thing, although they may be a bit more sophisticated about it. If something is bothering you or causing you pain," Chedva proposed, "that is your 'red triangle' and it is your job to conceal it lest it dominate your life and prevent you from contributing to others. You can draw all around it, or build upon it, but never let it occupy the entire picture by itself."

TO DRIVE HOME her message, she frequently employed her most powerful device: stories. Whether amusing, provocative or enlightening — or all three — her true-to-life tales were always food for thought (and action). Chedva also drew upon the rabbinical principle of *middah k'neged middah*, measure for measure. "If we neither speak nor listen to *lashon hara*, then God will not wish to hear *lashon hara* about us."

A woman who attended one of her talks once demanded a special dispensation, claiming that she was unable to survive even one hour without *lashon hara*. "Gossip is my life!" she pleaded in self-defense.

"Then take upon yourself fifteen minutes," Chedva bargained.

"No," the woman insisted, "not even that. I won't know what to do with myself for that quarter hour."

Just one day later, this "Yenta" called Chedva to relate that she had resolved to go the entire *day* without uttering *lashon hara*. Chedva was both ecstatic and incredulous. "What happened?" she asked.

"You contaminated the entire neighborhood, that's what happened!" the woman countered. "No one wants to speak to me. Whenever I phone someone, she invariably tells me that she has just begun her *lashon hara*-free hour and hangs up. And whenever someone calls me, she is as brief as possible and a second later the line goes dead!

"I simply have no one to talk to. Look what you've done!

"But I'll tell you the truth, there's a bright side to all this: I never knew I had so much time before. My husband blesses you just for the housework that I have managed to accomplish in all my newfound free time..."

ONE NEW YORKER was so smitten with her new lifestyle that she called her sister in Toronto and told her, "In New York we don't speak *lashon hara* anymore. Why don't you invite Chedva to Canada so that you too can enjoy a *lashon hara*-free environment?" Of course, her sister did, and Chedva obligingly flew to Toronto and spoke about crossing the narrow bridge, about striving for a better life, and about her Rebbe.

Chedva was a true disciple of the Chafetz Chaim; although she never articulated her relationship as such, it was standard for her to quote her Rebbe constantly.

"Wherever the Chafetz Chaim traveled, he would peddle his classic work detailing the laws and concepts of *shemiras halashon*, from which he earned his most fitting sobriquet. Naturally, it wasn't always an easy or dignified way to make a living. So when a kindhearted man noticed the difficulties the Chafetz Chaim was having, he offered to sell the books on the sage's behalf.

"Not much later, however, the Chafetz Chaim saw his agent arguing heatedly with a prospective buyer. Understandably dismayed, the Chafetz Chaim politely but promptly disenfranchised this franchise. '*Shemiras halashon* is a *zechus*,' he gently explained. 'It should not be forced on anyone.'"

"The Chafetz Chaim would give a discount to whoever pledged to learn from his book. Consider," Chedva added, with a reflective note to her voice, "how much we need discounts from Heaven..."

S INCE CHEDVA addressed only female audiences, she peppered her talks with examples women could readily relate to.

"One day a four-year-old Jerusalem girl had a terrible accident: her finger was cut off by a steel door. She was rushed from her kindergarten to the hospital where a surgeon prepared to sew the finger back on. A sympathetic anesthesiologist spoke to his young patient as the medication began to take effect.

"'Tell me who shut the door on your finger,' the doctor urged.

"'How can I tell you?' the child replied. 'It would be *lashon hara*, and I'm sure she didn't do it on purpose.'

"'I won't tell anyone,' the doctor assured the little girl as she drifted in and out of consciousness. 'I don't want to punish her, I just want to know who did it.'

"'But I can't tell you,' she insisted.

"The doctor simply could not understand the child's obstinacy. 'I promise you, I'll keep it a secret and no one will hear.'

"'Ahh, but God will,' the child responded."

SOMETIMES Chedva tried to reason with her audience. "I don't even understand what there is to speak *lashon hara* about! People say there is discord and baseless hatred among the Jews, but I disagree. Look how many people — *Chassidim, Misnagdim, Ashkenazim, Sephardim,* you name it — all extend themselves for me, a total stranger."

Just as Chedva could not grasp why everyone

loved her and wanted so much to help her, her incredible humility and self-effacing nature left her at a loss to fathom why Providence had placed her in the limelight. Although she did not feel great enough to actually *request* suffering like Rabbi Amnon or Nachum Ish Gam Zu, once it was thrust upon her, she had no complaints. "I thank God for the opportunity to repent completely," she would to say.

Nonetheless, she used the privilege of the podium to beg both friends and strangers to take precautions to ensure that they would never have to undergo a similar fate in order to arrive at the same realization. "Pray that you will never suffer, that you will be able to reach sublime levels of service to God in good health and without pain. Have the foresight to prepare the cure before the ailment, and fulfill the mission the Almighty has entrusted to you.

"Every one of us was created to serve the Lord whether in sickness or in health. My job is to serve Him in sickness. Pray that you will never be in my place."

Part of recognizing one's own place, Chedva contended, lay in appreciating what one has. She often related how her young children's incessant crying at night robbed her of sleep, and how, like every other mother, she found it very draining and dreamed of the day her babies would sleep through the night.

Once she was hospitalized, however, and besieged with pain and fever, her perspective changed. "If only my babies were keeping me awake now," she thought wistfully. "I'll never bemoan my sleepless nights at home again. I would dance to attend them!"

C HEDVA used the written word as a steady substitute for oral expression, a talent that would later yield rich dividends when she was no longer able to speak. Chedva was blessed with a felicity of style which found expression in moving poetry. Reading her poems, especially the originals written in her graceful handwriting, is like seeing a beautiful soul spilled onto paper.

Chedva wrote a letter to her "sisters," her term for the women she encountered, and it is an inspiring testament to the wellsprings of her emotions.

"My sisters, be careful with our special mitzvah of *tznius,* for its every component is a *zechus.* Do not abuse the privilege of covering your hair while you still have it," she wrote in a subtle but poignant allusion to the ravages of chemotherapy.

"At times you are lax about covering your elbows, as *halachah* requires. I know, of course, that you do not err intentionally, but the sleeve simply slips up during household chores.

"Because my veins have been weakened by radiation, the nurses must prick my skin repeatedly until they find a vein that will accept the IV. Accordingly, my arms are replete with contusions from the wrists up. Because of the bruised skin and the damaged veins the nurses have exhausted near my wrists, they are constantly working their way up my arms, exposing my elbows.

"I likewise tremble at being unable to wear stockings. My sisters, I implore you to exercise caution in this sacred task. Modesty is such an exalted privilege that it is shameful to neglect it."

EVEN AFTER extensive treatment, the advance of Chedva's disease was no less apparent. But although her body faltered, her mind shifted into overdrive. In rapid succession she contrived more concepts to benefit others, and every day she awoke from her hospital bed with a different idea.

One morning she declared with great ecstasy, "Let us all bear in mind God's honor when we recite a blessing." This simple thought cheered her immensely for it improved the quality of her blessings.

The following morning she awoke and beckoned her mother with great urgency, "Please instruct me to do some little thing. This way I fulfill the mitzvah of honoring my parents, and you will perform the mitzvah of *chessed* by obliging me. Imagine! We will be enveloped in *mitzvos*!"

The thought of being surrounded by *mitzvos* and *zechuyos* obsessed Chedva. When she could no longer speak and her hospital room was inundated with gift boxes of chocolate, she said in a frustrated whisper, "I don't need chocolate; I need *gemilus chassadim!*" As these words left her parched mouth, her wan, pale face suddenly became radiant.

Summoning her every ounce of strength, she strung a line above her bed on which to clip baby clothing, thus inaugurating a unique *gemach* for needy families in Israel.

Overnight her hospital room *gemach* burgeoned into a full-blown operation. Cartons and sacks of clothing were shipped to Israel, care of Chedva. The response was as enthusiastic as the reaction to her anti-*lashon hara* campaign had been. Affluent and even impoverished families all across North America eagerly participated in this project. Chedva insisted on personally overseeing all the sorting, processing, and distribution of the clothing, banishing her lingering managerial insecurity, amid the vehement protests of her loved ones.

"I can't simply lie in bed thinking about myself," she objected. "I must spend my last precious moments helping *klal Yisrael*! Let others take morphine," she declared. "I'll take *gemachim.*"

IF EVER anyone clung to the privilege of living, it was Chedva Silberfarb. She fought for every moment, yet she was remarkably unafraid to die. She publicly thanked God for giving her the opportunity to prepare for her own demise. "As long as there is still breath left within me," she said, paraphrasing the liturgy, "I shall gratefully thank the Lord and take advantage of every moment of life."

This is precisely what Chedva did throughout her twenty-seven short years. Most of what the public knows about Chedva is culled from her last two years, but for family and friends, those twenty-four months were but the ineluctable culmination of an exceedingly full life. It was as if she had always had a prescient awareness that her time on this earth would be all too fleeting and she must not waste a single precious moment of it.

WHEN THE students of Rabbi Akiva were forced to witness their beloved master's martyrdom, they asked in wide-eyed wonder, "Rebbe, how can you look so serene at a moment like this?" Rabbi Akiva responded, "All my days I regretted that I was never able to fulfill the injunction to 'love the Lord your God with all your soul' with the fullest intent. Now that I have the opportunity to fulfill this lofty concept, should I not rejoice?"

The key to Rabbi Akiva's joy — and his ability to withstand his torment — was that "all his days" were spent in preparation for his final triumphant moment. The same could be said for Chedva. Even as a young child dutifully visiting her grandfather in the hospital, the nurses were very much taken with the little girl. They nicknamed her "the girl with the golden hair and the golden heart."

Because of Chedva's sensitive skin, her mother had relieved her of kitchen detail at an early age. Nonetheless, Chedva always found a way of surreptitiously doing more than her share of kitchen chores, as evidenced by her rash-red hands. Similarly, she would steal away from her house to wash dishes for the Zacks family, who lived nearby. Instinctively drawn to the Zacks family, descendants of the Chafetz Chaim, she thrilled to her neighbors' authentic stories about their illustrious forebear.

Unlike other children, Chedva passed up the revelry of *Simchas Torah* in the synagogue. Although witnessing the marvelously joyous scene of *hakafos* was a tempting attraction, she preferred to spend the time with her bedridden grandmother.

When she learned that a neighbor, the mother of a brain-damaged child, was about to give birth, she scooped the child up in her arms and insisted on babysitting until further notice. When she showed up at her own doorstep with the child in tow and requested temporary lodging for her charge, her parents naturally agreed, and weren't at all surprised by their daughter's latest project.

At her *Shabbos kallah*, a day traditionally devoted to singing and merriment, Chedva had opted for a different form of celebration: she invited a single friend to join her in a day devoted to the recitation of *Tehillim.*

This, too, was no surprise to her mother, who had often discovered uneaten lunches in her daughter's schoolbag. Even as a young girl, Chedva had allocated her lunch period to extra prayer. "It is my greatest enjoyment," she claimed, and she could never indulge enough.

Years later, lying in her hospital bed too weak to pray, Chedva managed to articulate a four-word liturgy that the Baal Shem Tov would certainly have admired for its pietistic sincerity: "Abba, Abba; Abba, ABBA!" As Chedva later explained, she was confident that God would understand her supplication, "just as a mother senses her baby's needs before he can express them."

Similarly, she once reflected to her husband, "Consider how many chapters of *Tehillim* have been said on my behalf. I am sure that if they won't help me, they will definitely help you, and if not you, then our children, and if not our children, then certainly the Jewish people!"

ONE OF THE many virtues possessed by the Woman of Valor portrayed in Proverbs is her ability to "greet her very last day without fear." Since her life is filled with so many righteous deeds and accomplishments she has nothing to fear, and greets her final day with a laugh.

Chedva greeted her ascent to the Heavenly Assembly with a smile and with dignity. Enclothed in a weak body racked with pain, she could no longer speak and could barely walk. She was nevertheless determined to attend the Bar Mitzvah of her American hostess' son, even if it meant arriving at the very end. Her husband, however, was reluctant to precede her as it meant abandoning Chedva for what might be her final moments. Chedva perceived his dilemma and, unable to communicate orally, motioned with her hand, "Go. Go to the *simchah* and increase their joy. God willing, I will come, too."

A bit later, Chedva was indeed helped out of bed to shower and dress. Suddenly a violent spasm overcame her and she coughed up large quantities of blood. Somehow Chedva got hold of herself long enough to pen her final message. Although not as lyrical as her other compositions, this too was a poem of sorts, a brief ode to the grandeur of a holy soul whose every movement and thought were sensitive and refined.

In the same beautiful handwriting that graced all her work, she wrote: "I thank God that I was able to shower and clean up the mess I made."

And then: "My pulse is quickening. Please strengthen me, in order that everything will be all right and I will yet be well."

Even when a sharp sword is poised at your neck, the Talmud teaches, one must still trust in God and hope for survival. And Chedva did.

Like everyone else, she was imbued with a pure soul, but unlike many, this is exactly what Chedva Silberfarb returned to her Maker. With a smile on her lips and a tranquil countenance, she breathed her final breath, rejoicing to her very last day.

NEWS OF Chedva's passing was greeted with grief and anguish, sending shockwaves throughout the Jewish world. *Chassidim, Misnagdim,* the devout and the not-yet religious — all were moved to tears over the passing of the mother of the *shemiras halashon* renaissance. One simple woman lamented: "She never asked us for money; all she wanted was for us to guard our tongue."

And for this she will always be remembered. In

the streets of Jerusalem and Bnei Brak, awe-struck children spread the grim tidings: "Do you know who passed away? '*Chedva Shemiras Halashon.*'"

Her name, just like the Chafetz Chaim's, has become synonymous with the concept of guarding one's tongue. Indeed, as her husband pointed out at the funeral, the sum of the Chafetz Chaim's long life span of 93 plus Chedva's short one of 27 together added up to the very symbol of longevity awarded to those who refrain from guile and slander: 120.

Just twenty-seven years old, the mother of three children and a worldwide movement, Chedva Silberfarb crossed the bridge and left the world a more beautiful place than she entered it.

Heard from: Rebbetzins Sarah Angel and Rivka Plitnick

Where There's a Will, There's a Way

MAX, rest yourself. You've got to save your strength."

"What for? My time's almost up. You know it. The doctors know it. And I know it, too."

"Stop saying that, will you? Your doctors say you're gonna be all right."

"Ha! What do they know? I'm the one who's sick! Did you find my three kids?"

"I'm trying. Max, I'm your friend and your lawyer, but a detective I'm not. So give me a few days."

"I'm the one who's dying and I'm supposed to give you a few days? Did you update my will?"

"Of course, all fifty-four times you told me."

"Well, make it fifty-five. I like even numbers."

"That's odd."

"You're not kidding. When my wife went, the whole world turned out. Now I can't even get a *minyan*! Did you try Fort Lauderdale? I think they went to Fort Lauderdale."

"Karen's roommate said she went to Daytona Beach. I've got the police looking for her."

"What about Richard and Sammie?"

"Richard's skiing in Sun Valley. Sammie's playing golf out in Arizona."

"Don't they know how sick I am?"

"Yes, but the doctors..."

"The doctors. You and the doctors. Listen to me. When I became Max Kling, the Felt Cap King, I made four million. Every cent came from playing *my* hunches, not those of the hat business, show business *or* the medical business. So when I'm telling you it's *my* turn to go, believe me, it's my turn. After all the grief they've given me, I'm looking forward to a little peace and quiet. Did you find my will yet? Here's what I'm gonna do..."

☙

WHEN RABBI ARTHUR MOSKOWITZ became the Executive Director of the Darchei Torah Yeshivah, he had no idea what he was in for. As far as he knew, this yeshivah was no different from most of its brethren in America: spiritually affluent but materially impoverished. Little did Moskowitz realize how impoverished it truly was.

The previous E.D. had lasted only six months, and Moskowitz wondered how he had lasted that long. The job was a "mission impossible." The mailing list was so old, the yeshivah was still using 18-cent stamps! How they managed to pay teachers was anyone's guess. And the utilities! The cut-off notices came before the bills. It was as if the electric company were saying: "We know you can't pay this anyway, so why should we waste our time telling you how much you owe?"

Darchei Torah, like most yeshivas, survived on loans. Thanks to a friendly banker, Rob (Reuven) Levinson, the yeshivah had managed to borrow $100,000. Best of all, the loan had been open-ended and — for a while — the yeshivah had only had to pay interest. This benevolent loan had been negotiated several years before the scrutiny days which followed the Savings and Loan fiasco. Now Reuven Levinson's bank was going after as many outstanding debts as possible, and one of the most outstanding was the $100,000 note from the Darchei Torah Yeshivah.

The bank awarded the yeshivah six months to come up with the money. Half a year. It was a hopeless task. Still, Rabbi Arthur Moskowitz was determined to give it his best shot. If he couldn't reach his goal, he could at least prove to the bank that he was trying.

The first principle in the fundraiser's guide to fundraising was to produce a letter that spelled out the situation in no uncertain terms.

Yeshivah Darchei Torah
801 East 26th St.
Brooklyn, NY 11210

25 Tishrei 5750
October 24, 1989

Dear Friend,

If you were to see a person who was drowning, would you simply walk on by?

Well, the Darchei Torah Yeshivah is drowning. Our debts have exceeded $100,000. We can't continue without collecting additional funds. And we can't collect additional funds without your help.

I know we've appealed to your generosity in the past. And I know you have responded warmly, with a full and open hand. Yet now we ask again, because, frankly, we have nowhere else to turn.

Please, please keep the light of Torah burning. Send whatever you can afford. Now. Because without your help, the doors of Darchei Torah Yeshivah will close forever, God forbid.

Sincerely yours,

Rabbi Arthur Moskowitz
Executive Director

IT WAS A STRONG LETTER, maybe too strong; but there was no other choice. Along with the letter, Rabbi Moskowitz enclosed an updated list of expenses, a nasty letter from the bank (they were happy to oblige) and a return envelope.

The Executive Director sent his appeal to every man, woman and child ("Who knows? Maybe they get a big allowance!") on his mailing list. Then he waited.

To his surprise and amazement, the letter started working. Checks came in. Big checks. Little checks. *Pushka* contents. Savings bonds. Even bank notes of various denominations.

It was as if the Lord had blessed his letter and it had found favor in the eyes of all who received it. After three weeks, Rabbi Moskowitz had received more than $28,000, plus pledges for $6,000 more.

"Good news and bad news today, Rabbi," said Sara, his secretary and administrative assistant, as he walked into his office one morning.

"What's the good news?"

"We received fourteen more checks in today's mail."

"Great! And the bad news?"

"They total seventy-six dollars and twenty-five cents."

"That's all? From fourteen checks?" Rabbi Moskowitz slumped heavily into his chair.

"Sorry, Rabbi."

Seventy-six dollars today. One hundred and thirty dollars yesterday. Eighty-two dollars the day before. The checks were finally beginning to taper off. The young Executive Director knew it was time to try something else, but what?

"A Half-Baked Sale!" suggested Mrs. Adelman, the chairperson of the PTA.

"A 'Half-Baked Sale'?" Rabbi Moskowitz echoed uncomprehendingly.

"Sure," Mrs. A. explained. "We'll get half the parents in the school to bake something, and the other half to buy it. If every family sells just $50 worth of baked goods, we'll have made $10,000 in one evening!"

It was a wild idea, but Moskowitz couldn't cook up anything better.

A T MRS. ADELMAN'S URGING, half the yeshivah mothers got onto the production end of gastronomic adventure, culinary indulgence, and sheer sybaritic joy. For two solid weeks they baked chocolate cookies, almond cookies, butter cookies, cookies with stripes, cookies with sprinkles, apple, cherry, banana and cream pies, seven-layer cakes, five-layer cakes, three-layer cakes. Fourteen days later, there were so many sweets you could get cavities just looking at it all.

The bake sale was called for seven o'clock Wednesday night. By 8:30 PM, both Mrs. Adelman and Rabbi Moskowitz knew they had a problem.

There were plenty of spectators but no one was buying.

Rabbi Moskowitz steered himself through the obstacle course of table after table laden with goodies. There were hundreds and hundreds of cookies. Scores of cakes. Dozens of pies. All sitting untouched. It was as if the whole town had suddenly gone on a diet!

"What's wrong?" he asked one of his students. "Don't you like these cookies? Try some. Better yet, *buy* some!"

"Are you kidding? I can't even look at another cookie, much less eat one. Every day, the guys have been bringing samples to school. I guess I've OD'd on flour, sugar and eggs."

EVEN THE FATHERS were no help. They just walked around muttering "Cholesterol and calories. Cholesterol and calories." Rabbi Moskowitz had a sneaking suspicion that every husband was afraid to compliment, let alone enjoy, someone else's wife's baking. If they were forbidden to enjoy them, what was the point of shelling out good money for all the cholesterol and calories?

The result was that the entire affair ended up being a real bitter-sweet disaster. For days, the cooks in the cafeteria valiantly tried to serve the leftovers. They turned brownies into "chocolate bread pudding," and for nourishment turned over the inside of apple turnovers. By the time Purim rolled around, no one could even think about pastry without getting a stomach ache!

Now there were just five weeks left. And Rabbi Arthur Moskowitz was still $63,000 in the hole.

THERE WAS ONLY ONE THING left to do: go see Murray Segal for a loan, or maybe a grant or a gift. Murray was one of the most generous *baalei tzedakah* on the Eastern seaboard. His lighting fixture store in Connecticut was on every *meshulach*'s list from Bangor, Maine to Bangkok, Thailand. Arthur mused: "So many guys go there, the Greyhound bus stops routinely at his store! It's probably even listed on their bus schedule!"

But he had to try, even if he'd be one out of hundreds. The Executive Director stuck his head out of the crowded cubicle he used for an office. "Sara," he called, "phone Mr. Segal for me, please."

A few seconds later, Sara answered, "Rabbi, I've got Mr. Segal on the line."

Arthur picked up the phone and tried to sound more cheerful than he felt. He reminded himself of the key to successful fundraising — make the other guy think you're doing *him* a favor. And above all, be cheerful.

"Hello, Reb Murray!" he greeted Segal with strenuous joviality.

"Rabbi Moskowitz! It's good to hear your voice. Can I interest you in a lighting fixture? Perhaps a chandelier for your yeshivah?"

Arthur laughed as hard as he could manage. "No, but if you want to donate one, we'll accept!

Actually, I'm calling to give you an opportunity to invest... in a mitzvah! Our yeshivah could use a little extra help."

"You mean teach? Well, I don't know..."

Arthur laughed again. It took even more effort this time. "Maybe you could give us lessons in making money! Seriously, is it possible to see you?"

"Well, there's no harm in talking. Come on by tomorrow. Say two-ish."

The Executive Director's mouth was still stretched into a fixed grin as he replaced the receiver.

THE NEXT DAY, Rabbi Arthur Moskowitz got in his 1978 vintage Pontiac for the ninety-minute drive up Interstate 95 to Connecticut. Route 95 is the main highway running up and down the east coast. In the earlier days of American travel, it had a different name and over the years, in the interest of progress and efficiency, it's been renamed a few times. First it was known as the "Boston Post Road." Next it became "U.S. Route One." Finally, it evolved into "I-Ninety-Five." Along the way, a lot was lost. Instead of meandering through the rural towns and quaint villages that dot the east coast, instead of savoring the lives and lifestyles of those who reside there, instead of getting a real feel for America, you can now speed along the eight-laned ribbon of asphalt and not have to feel, taste or even see a thing. On a good day, that is.

If there is construction on the road or, Heaven forbid, an accident has occurred, you might be stuck in the same spot for hours. That's on a bad day. Even the rest stops have changed over the years. The corporation famous for making hamburgers identical in every way all over the country did exactly the same thing for architecture. Even the bathrooms have been done in the standard mind-numbing decor. And to make matters worse, you have to pay for the privilege.

About halfway through Rabbi Moskowitz's trip, he had to avail himself — pardon the indelicacy — of one of these "spotlessly clean" restrooms.

"There's a rest stop up ahead," he reminded himself.

THE RABBI slowly guided his car off the highway and up the exit ramp. Rather than park in one of the lots, he pulled up in the fire lane in front of the restaurant. As he shut off the motor and prepared to get out, he saw the sign. "Pardon our construction. Bathrooms out of order."

Arthur turned the ignition on and headed back to the highway. Fifteen miles later, he spotted a road sign that read "Turkeyfoot Rd. Exit 4 miles," followed by a second sign, "Rest area $4\frac{1}{2}$ miles."

"That's what I'm looking for," Moskowitz noted with a sigh. He urged his car forward to make the miles and the minutes go faster. As the exit ramp came into view, he swung into the lane that led off the highway. Rabbi Moskowitz was already off the ramp before he realized he'd made a mistake.

He had taken the wrong turn. Rabbi Arthur Moskowitz was now heading *east* on Turkeyfoot Rd. It was a narrow, rutted, soft-shouldered roadway that seemed to lead miles away from the nearest anything. A few mailboxes stood like sentries by the side of the road. An abandoned farmhouse, untended fields and scrub brush and an occasional billboard ("Stake yourself to dinner at Wayne's Steakhouse!") dotted the landscape.

Frantically, Rabbi Moskowitz tried to find either a place to execute a U-turn or, better yet, a gas station where he could get directions and use the facilities.

A S LUCK WOULD HAVE IT, or rather, would *not* have it, there were no gas stations in sight. Five minutes passed. Ten minutes passed. Fifteen minutes passed. And with each passing minute, he got farther and farther from civilization, the call of nature and his two o'clock appointment with Segal.

Finally, to Arthur's amazement he saw what looked like it might be a synagogue up ahead! It was a two-story wood frame building surrounded by a high brick wall. There was an unmistakably Jewish sign, but it was too far away for Rabbi Moskowitz to read. Still, it meant his journey was nearing a happy end. "Thank God, I'm saved!" he thought gratefully.

One block away from the building, he read the hewn stone:

Bnai Zion Cemetery

"Shrek-and-a-half!" he exclaimed. "Well, maybe there's someone in there." As soon as he got out of his car, he saw several other vehicles and a hearse parked behind the building.

Arthur dashed up the steps and knocked at the entrance. A man who was obviously a mortician opened the door solemnly, and bowed silently.

"Are you here for the Kling funeral?" he asked unctuously.

For a minute, Rabbi Moskowitz was too stunned to answer. "Uh, I-I suppose so," he mumbled and stepped inside.

After visiting the facilities, Arthur peeked into the chapel. It was small, with a capacity of forty at most. Five straight rows of plain wooden benches led up to the front where an expensive looking wooden casket lay in state. About fifteen men and women stood about. Rabbi Moskowitz didn't see anyone under 60 years of age. "Well," he thought, "this must be why Hashem sent me here — to help make a *minyan*!"

The mortician approached the Rabbi. "Please sign the guest book," he requested gravely. Rabbi Moskowitz dutifully scribbled his name and the name of the yeshivah.

"Is there a phone here?" he asked the man in black. "I have to make a very important call."

"No, I'm afraid not," the mortician replied. "But the first left at the next intersection will bring you to the rear of the highway rest stop. There are several pay phones inside the building."

THIRTY-FIVE minutes later, Rabbi Moskowitz made a quick call to Murray Segal. Fifty-five minutes later, he was seated in front of the *baal tzedakah* himself. "Sorry I'm late..." he apologized for the third time.

"Don't worry about it," Murray said cordially. "What can I do for you?"

The Executive Director of Darchei Torah went through the institution's entire financial situation, good faith, bad debts and all. (The story was so depressing he gave up all pretence of being cheerful.) Mr. Segal listened politely, but Arthur could tell that while he was concerned, he was not convinced.

At the end of the presentation, Murray unfolded his hands from across his chest and began in a soft tone. "Arthur, I'd love to be able to help you," he said. "I really would. But there's no way I can spend that kind of money. The best I can do is a thousand right now. In a couple of months, maybe I could give you another check. But believe me, your debts don't compare to mine."

Rabbi Moskowitz felt his heart sink to his shoes. "Perhaps you could host a parlor meeting, or call up a few of your friends..." he implored.

"I've done what I can do. Honest," Segal said firmly. With that, the president of Segal's Lighting Center stood up. "Have me in mind when you're learning," he said, extending a hand and a signed check. "Maybe we'll both get rich."

All the way home, Arthur reviewed his talk. "If only I had said this or said that... it would have been different. Maybe the fact that I was late. Maybe I should have brought some students along..." The "ifs" and "maybes" played havoc with his digestive system.

FOR THE NEXT FEW WEEKS, Rabbi Moskowitz begged, borrowed and bargained his debt down. He spoke. He wrote. He called. If there was a way to earn a dollar, he found it. Still, things looked bleak. He had forty thousand to raise with only two weeks to go. "*Tracht goot, vet zein goot*," the Yiddish expression went. "Think good and it will be good." Although Rabbi Moskowitz had always believed this, he was beginning to have his doubts.

"The bank will understand," he told Sara. "They'll see I'm trying. Won't they?" Then it hit him. The bank! That was it. He had forgotten all about the fact that he'd paid off 60% of the debt. Surely they would take that into account. And if they could give him another few months, why, he was sure he could manage the rest.

With trembling hands and a quavering voice, Rabbi Arthur Moskowitz telephoned Reuven Levinson.

"First Federal Bank and Trust," said the operator matter-of-factly.

"Reu... I mean Rob Levinson, please."

"I'm sorry, Mr. Levinson no longer works here," she reported icily.

"What?" Arthur exclaimed incredulously.

"Yes, Mr. Levinson left about three weeks ago.

Could I connect you with someone else in the loan department?"

"Er, yes, please."

T HREE SECRETARIES and two minutes of "Symphony of Sounds" later, Rabbi Moskowitz was connected to Mr. Peter J. Stevenson, First Federal's Assistant Vice President. Speaking rapidly, the young Rabbi packed the last five-and-a-half months of blood, sweat and tears into five-and-a-half minutes. In return, he got a vague assurance of "I'll see what I can do and get back to you."

Later that afternoon, the phone rang. "It's a Mr. Stevenson," Sara said.

"Thank you, Sara," Arthur called out and lifted the receiver.

"Rabbi Moskowitz?"

"Yes, Mr. Stevenson. I didn't expect you to call so soon."

"Well, I wanted to inform you as soon as I could. I contacted Mr. Leonetti, our Senior Vice President in charge of collections."

"Uh, oh," thought Arthur. "Here it comes." Then he asked, "What did Mr. Leonetti say?"

"He regrets that he cannot allow your school any more time. It would set a bad precedent and open the bank up to charges of favoritism."

"But doesn't he realize the unfavorable publicity the bank will receive when you close the school down?"

"He's aware of that. But he feels that if the public knows that the bank has done all it can, then people will understand."

"Which 'people' — other bankers?" Arthur snapped angrily.

"Rabbi, I'm sorry. But our deadline remains unchanged. If I can be of any further assistance, please don't hesitate to call. Good day." And with that, Assistant Vice President Peter J. Stevenson hung up. Arthur did the same ten seconds later, still in shock.

I TRIED, HASHEM," Arthur said out loud. "I really did. I guess it's Your will that we start over." He sank into a despondent reverie, thinking about his dashed hopes for the yeshivah.

"Mail's here!" Sara called out, rousing him from his contemplations.

"Anything worth looking at?" Rabbi Moskowitz asked sadly.

"A circular from *Torah U'Mesorah*. Four appeals for money."

"Hah!" Arthur laughed bitterly.

"And a letter from a lawyer."

"The bank has probably started foreclosure proceedings already," Arthur said to no one in particular. "Fast work, huh?"

H E TOOK THE ENVELOPE and ripped it open. The first piece of paper that slid out had a gold-embossed design that looked very expensive. The letterhead read: Morton L. Bauer, Esquire, Attorney-at-law. His message was brief.

March 19, 1990

Rabbi Arthur Moskowitz
Yeshivah Darchei Torah
801 East 26th St.
Brooklyn, NY 11210

Dear Rabbi Moskowitz:

I have been instructed on behalf of the estate of the late Max Kling to divide his assets among all those who attended his funeral. Your share is enclosed.

Sincerely,

Morton L. Bauer, Esq.

The second piece of paper was a certified check. It was made out to Rabbi Arthur Moskowitz. The young Rabbi looked. And looked. Suddenly staid and placid Arthur Moskowitz was dancing a jig.

Her jaw gaping, Sara gawked at her boss, who was leaping onto his desk. She finally noticed that his right hand was waving what looked like a check and he was singing "Three Cheers for the Red, White and Blue."

The euphoric Executive Director gave the certified bank order a resounding buss and presented it for his secretary's perusal. It *was* a check, for $52,430.

"But, what...I mean when...?" She stammered in confusion at the enormous figure. "I mean, how did you do it?"

The Rabbi smiled, without straining for once. "I guess it was a Providential twist of serendipity: a matter of being in the wrong place at the right time."

Heard from: Dr. Yossi Scheller

THREE

The Best Defense

THE Austro-Hungarian Empire shortly before its demise. Its ruler? Franz Jozef of the Hapsburg Dynasty.

A good place, or at least as good a place as any east of Essex and Delancey, to wait for *Mashiach*. Jews and Gentiles, *Zhidin* and *goyim* as they are fond of referring to each other in their more candid moments, get along, well, let's say, not badly. The devoutly Catholic Franz Jozef takes a benevolent, if not downright friendly, attitude toward his Jews (whose official legal status for longer than can be remembered has been "Servants of the Treasury").

When an anti-Semitic member of the court of the Holy Roman Emperor and the King of Jerusalem (yes, this is the title of the Hapsburg rulers) tries to incite his sovereign against the Jewish subjects of the realm, he decides to show His Majesty just how silly and stupid, pedantic and petty, odd and obscurantist are those who killed and every day again kill "our lord." He sends his staff out to study the Jewish texts and bring him samples to prove his point. After weeks of searching it is agreed that the fourth article of the second chapter of a Jewish text known as *Orach Chaim* will be shown to His Majesty.

"Your Machesty, I sought zis might interest you."

"Vat is it, Heinz?"

"It is vun of zose dusty old books zat ze Chews are alvays studying."

"Ah, yes certainly."

"Read zis, Your Machesty."

"But, Heinz, as you vell know, ze King of Jerusalem does not read Hebrew."

"See here, Your Machesty, I have prepared a translation."

"Good for you, Heinz. But let me achust my monocle.

'He shall first don his right shoe and not tie it; aftervuds, he shall don his left shoe, tie it, and zen return and tie his right shoe.'

"Vy, Heinz, zis is extraordinary! Vat precision! Vat attention to detail! Ze Chews have a manual zat tells zem how to put on each article of clozing. Yes, Heinz, I agree vis you zat zey are an extraordinary pipple. In fact, after I read somesing as inspiring as zis, I sometimes regret zat ve Christians aren't Chewish!"

A S GOOD A PLACE as any to wait for *Mashiach.* Anti-Semitism is only popular, not official, and the ruler, unlike so many of his subjects, can be approached *and* reasoned with. Matters, as everyone realizes, could be, oh, so much worse.

Under the enlightened reign of Franz Jozef, the State Prosecutor of Tarnov is not only Jewish, but conspicuously observant. Known among the Gentiles as Herr Kaganoff and among the Jews simply as Reb Eliyahu, he is disgusted though not surprised by this morning's discovery.

Overnight his doorpost, lintel, *mezuzah,* and most relevantly, threshold before them have been daubed liberally with pig excrement (a product quite plentiful in this sector of the great Hapsburg empire). As a learned Jew, he has always realized that the situation — good as it is — is only as good as can be expected while waiting for *Mashiach,* and just as easily could deteriorate. The case he will have to prosecute next week is tailor-made for the town's hotheads, and he has known all along that it is only a matter of time before the personal harassment begins.

❀

"Vladislav, my friend, come let me buy you a drink!"

"Buy me a drink, Boleslav? Why?"

"Come sit down, Vladislav. I will tell you. But first fill up your glass. Now drink. That's right. All of it. Good vodka, no?"

"I don't know, my good friend Boleslav. I can never tell after just one drink."

"Nor can I, Vladislav. Nor can I. But when you've caught up to me, you will agree that it is good vodka. Here, have another."

"I thank you, Boleslav, but why so generous, and on a weekday?"

"Well, Vladislav, you know that mare of mine?"

"Yes, Boleslav, I know her well, and a fine-looking animal she is!"

"Very well put, Vladislav, very well put. She is indeed a fine-*looking* animal."

"A fine-looking animal indeed. Could I have a bit more?"

"Of course, Vladishlav, pash me your glash. And now my glash. There... Anyway, you were shaying that my mare izh a fine-looking animal, were you not?"

"I was, yes."

"And sho, Vladishlav?"

"Your mare is a fine-looking animal, so why, dear Boleslav, why the generosity? Why are you spending so much money on vodka in the middle of the week?"

"Why, that is shimple, Vladishlav, becauzhe my mare, my fine-looking mare hazh jusht contracted tuberculoshish."

"Why, if your fine mare, whom you sho prizhe, hazh tuberculoshish, are you shelebrating here in the tavern?"

"Here, Vladishlav, have another. Oh, the bottle izh empty. I will ask the bartender to bring another. I will tell you why I am shele... shelebrating. Jusht a few dayzh ago my fine-looking mare contracted tubercu... tuberculoshish."

"Sho you shaid, Boleshlav."

"Yesh, Vladizhlub, but that izh only half the shtory."

"The shtory of your mare who caught tubercu... tubercu... got shick?"

"Quiet, Vladizh. How do you know that my mare has tubercu... tuber... got shick?! Don't breathe a word of thish to anyone; jusht today I shold her to a *Zhid!*"

"Bolezh, izh *that* why you are shelebrating?"

"Shelebrating what, Shtefan?"

STRANGE AS IT MAY SOUND, even a Polish pig farmer can have too much to drink, and although Thursday dawned crisp and clear, Vladi and Boli were in no state to appreciate it. Having regurgitated their way back home, both slept quite deeply.

As it happened, Vladi never did catch up with Boli, and as a result, whereas Boleslav's memory of the previous evening's events was virtually non-existent, Vladislav's was merely foggy. As Vladislav's bloodshot eyes began to focus and the rusty wheels inside his head began to turn, the pieces of his final conversation before turning into a jelly fish began falling into place. But the more pieces that fell in place, the stranger the whole thing seemed.

"Very well," he thought. "So Boleslav Mikalauskus tricks some Jew into buying a tubercular horse from him. So what? Everybody knows that the Jews of this town buy on credit and never pay until thirty days have passed. True, no one extends credit to us peasants; no one is that foolish. But everyone wants the Jews' business, and since they always pay up anyway, everyone extends credit. So what's the good of selling a sick horse? Before the month is out, that tight-fisted Jew will discover he's been cheated and simply refuse to pay.

"So where did all the money for the vodka come from?"

The morning was wasted anyway, and since hangovers love company, Vladislav decided to pay Boleslav a visit, to thank him for his largesse of the previous evening, and to straighten out the whole story in his mind.

Boleslav, it turned out, had had little difficulty, in his simple peasant way, working out the scam for unloading his tubercular mare on a Jew many times wealthier and better educated than himself. The Jew was essentially a trusting soul and not accustomed to being swindled by the local peasantry. The standard thirty-day delay in payment was usually an effective guarantee against defective merchandise, short supplies and the like, and as a result, the Gentiles rarely bothered trying to cheat the Jews.

THE JEWS, for their part, always paid their debts on time, and so a kind of grudging trust had grown between the two communities. Thus, when Boleslav invented his story of a sick wife and child and his desperate need for cash, his buyer did not think much about waiving the thirty-day delay and paying immediately. Boleslav concluded his tale proudly, "Let that filthy *Zhid* try and prove that my mare had tuberculosis before I sold it. He'll make a fool of himself before the entire town!"

Both Poles laughed heartily and helped themselves to another round of Boleslav's homemade hangover remedy. But while Boleslav's mind had gotten about as much of a workout as it could possibly stand working out how to swindle the Jew, Vladislav's mind began to shift gears.

"Boleslav, my dear friend, who was the *Zhid* whom you favored by selling him your prized mare at such a remarkably reasonable price?"

"Moshe Lishinsky."

"Lishinsky? Why he's the wealthiest man in town, that thieving crook!"

"Yes, he certainly is," laughed Boleslav. "He'll never even miss the money. Serves him right, the way those *Zhids* suck our blood."

"Tell me something, my friend. If I showed you a way to make him pay you *again* for your mare, would you give me half?"

"Vladislav! Of course I would, but that's impossible. How could I ever get him to pay me again? Why, right now (guffaw), that poor mare is probably dying away. He wouldn't give me another half zloty for her."

"But if he does pay, will you split the price with me?"

"I said I would. Do you think I am not trustworthy? Tell me how this can be done, and half the money is yours."

"Look here, Boleslav, it is quite simple. When thirty days have passed, we will go together to the home of Moshe Lishinsky and ask him to make payment for the horse."

"His house! If I come anywhere near there in the next ten years, he'll have me beaten!"

"My dear Boleslav, sometimes you are as thick as the animals you breed. We live in a civilized country. No Jew, no matter how wealthy, can have a God-fearing Christian beaten. And what if he does? So much the better for us."

"I still don't understand."

"Of course, you don't; you are too honest. Listen. Do not the Jews of this town always buy on credit and pay at the end of thirty days?"

"Yes, everyone knows that."

"So at the end of thirty days, you and I will go to your Jew and demand your payment."

"But..."

"But, you will say, he has already paid me, and in this you are correct. But let me ask you, dear Boleslav, did you write him out a receipt?"

"Vladislav, you know I can't write."

"Of course, you can't; neither can I. It is no coincidence that no one gives receipts in this town. So when he refuses to pay you, we will tell him that we will sue him in court. He will realize immediately that no one will believe that he paid you at the time of the sale."

"What will we do, Vladislav, if he still refuses?"

"Why we will take him to court, and we will win! And do you know who will win for us? That haughty Kaganoff. He will win for us! One Jew will go against another Jew in court; how can we lose?"

"Yes, Vladislav, I will do it!"

"Excellent. Shall we drink a toast to our new partnership?"

WHEN Reb Moshe Lishinsky discovered that his new mare was tubercular he toyed briefly with the idea of trying to recover his money. It didn't take him long to realize, however, that he had been foolish to pay cash and that he would never be able to prove that the animal had contracted the disease before the purchase. Relations with the local yokels were decent, thank God, and every Jew in the empire knew that if he was not circumspect, it was his own problem.

True, it was the reign of the benevolent Franz Jozef, but why stir up trouble? The natives were as bored as ever. Why give them the kind of entertainment they loved most? Take your medicine, Reb Moshe chided himself, and just don't make the same mistake in the future. Besides, the man had been dirt poor, his sick wife and hungry child needed the money far more than I. "Too bad," he sighed aloud, "he'll only drink it away in any case."

A rational and prudent way of accepting one's fate; waiting for *Mashiach*, after all, is no picnic. Be that as it may, Moshe's usual moderation and equanimity were severely tried when three weeks after putting the mare to sleep he was confronted by the collection agency of Boleslav and Vladislav, Inc.

Reb Moshe became indignant at the demand for additional payment. Although known to one and all as a wealthy *gvir*, Reb Moshe Lishinsky had grown up on a farm and had spent his entire life at physical labor; one might say he knew how to handle himself. So when Boli and Vladi, obviously fortified with "Polish courage," began to get nasty and threaten him with everything from a court case to a full-blown *pogrom*, Reb Moshe offered personally to escort them from his property;

and when the two men's contentiousness continued unabated, that was precisely what he did.

Lishinsky had faced down drunken Gentiles before, and their assurances that he would live to regret his actions did not cause him to lose even an instant of sleep. There were two factors that he had failed to consider, however. The first was that Vladislav Bratkowski was a little bit sharper than the average peasant. The second one was that he was a lot meaner.

Immediately after being shown the door, Boli and Vladi made a visit to the Chief of Police, and then to the local priest. Having then invested all of their venture capital, the two partners paid a visit to the tavern's executive corner where, aided by distilled mash of potato, they sat down to discuss pig futures.

⁂

"NOW, tell me once more, Reb Moshe. You say that you are certain that you paid this man?"

"Yes, of course, I paid him, Reb Eliyahu. Don't you believe me?"

"Of course, I believe you. But that's not the point. Have you no proof that will stand up in a court of law? No receipt? No, of course you have no receipt. No one in this town demands receipts. But why did you pay cash? Certainly a man of your experience..."

"Yes, I know. I know. But the man told me that he was pressed for cash. He went on and on, and it's been years since anyone in this town has tried to cheat me."

"But that's because you, like every other Jew, pay only after thirty days."

"I know, Reb Eliyahu. I know. Look, I'm willing to pay double. I just want to wash my hands of the whole thing."

"Yes, that would be wonderful. But the police have declared this a criminal matter, a case of fraud. I am obliged to prosecute you, and it is only on my say-so that you are not in jail at this very moment."

"I appreciate..."

"Don't be ridiculous. Why must you sit behind bars? You've done nothing wrong. But if only I could demonstrate in court who the real criminal is."

"That poor drunken Mikalauskus. I am certain that that hateful Bratkowski character put him up to this."

"Don't feel so sorry for Mikalauskus. He sold you a dying horse, and for full price, didn't he?"

"Yes, well..."

"Listen, Reb Moshe, the priest delivered a sermon on Judas Iscariot yesterday. And do you know what they did to my door last night?"

"I can guess. They did it to mine twice last week, and before that, they set fire to one of my fields."

"So you understand. And do you know what those two are saying around town? They're saying, 'It's not enough that the Jews suck our blood every day of the year, now they are stealing our animals as well!'"

"But surely, Reb Eliyahu, you could intercede. You are, after all, the State Prosecutor. Your competence and honesty are known throughout the district. You are the most admired Jew in town. If you were to dismiss the charges, no one would dare to question your judgment. I would pay those two hoodlums whatever they ask, just to be certain that the rest of the Jews in this town do not suffer."

"It is true that my colleagues and superiors would never question my actions to my face," Reb Eliyahu conceded, "but the mob, Reb Moshe! What about the mob? No, no. It is too late. Besides, the Archbishop has expressed his personal interest in this case, and he may even attend the proceedings."

"What are we to do?"

"I don't know, Reb Moshe. I don't know yet, but you must trust me."

"Why, that goes without saying!"

"No, no. I mean *really* trust me. You must remember, no matter what I do or say in court, I am acting in your and our best interest, and in the interest of justice."

"Reb Eliyahu, you don't have to tell me that."

"Yes, I do. Now, don't forget, and don't tell anyone of our conversation. And, Reb Moshe?"

"Yes?"

"No matter what happens, do not offer money to anyone, not to the judge, not to the Archbishop, and certainly not to those two hoodlums!"

IN RURAL AREAS the world over, the local court convened on market day, but the town of Tarnov had never in its history known a market day like this one. Since movies had not yet been invented and books were as rare as those who could read them, there was nothing like a real-life installment of *Tarnov Law* to alleviate the tedium of agrarian life; what's more, this was no regular installment.

Peasants by the wagonload began arriving before dawn. Whole families, complete with picnic lunches and ample liquid refreshment (of the distilled variety), converged around the post office building which also served as courthouse and jail. The courtroom, of course, was entirely too small, but in the land where *protektzia* was invented, determining who was and was not permitted in was relatively simple.

Round-faced, red-cheeked, sandy-haired relatives, friends, and cronies of the local two-man police department, along with a handful of wealthy Christians willing to pay for the privilege, packed the small spectators' gallery. The room reeked of human breath heavily laced with vapor of vodka, a fragrance that went all but unnoticed by everyone but the two Jews in the courtroom.

While inside the noise level was kept to a respectful murmur, outside was a different story.

Children shouted, peddlers hawked their wares, dogs barked, old ladies cursed as their husbands spat. Geese, chickens and ducks, bound for market, honked, cackled and quacked, respectively. Pigs and cattle, soon to be slaughtered, squealed and bellowed. Outside the air was also redolent of vodka, but added pungency was provided by the aroma of fresh manure.

To the Boleslavs, Vladislavs and Stanislavs of this world, the court proceedings were like a carnival. To a Jew, the crowd appeared anything but fun-loving. But then, of course, there was not a Jew to be found in greater Kalisz, excluding the defendant and the prosecutor. Those with relatives in distant towns had decided that this was a good time for a visit. Those who stayed behind, had locked and barred their doors. The Rabbi of the town had been fasting and praying since the night before.

The crowd split as an elegant carriage drawn by two white stallions came careening up to the post office, nearly trampling several children. Men bowed and women crossed themselves as the Archbishop stepped down, and several of the more eager believers ran up and kneeled to kiss their holy father's ring. As his eminence entered the cramped courtroom, the police chief's second cousin, hoping to secure his place in Heaven, vacated his front row seat in honor of the Church. Reb Moshe Lishinsky was led to the defendant's table.

REB ELIYAHU KAGANOFF knew well in advance what the town would look like on the day of the most important case of his life. He had, therefore, packed his wife off to her sister's house some fifty miles away, and advised Reb Moshe Lishinsky to do the same. To avoid the crowd, he had slept and recited his morning prayers in his tiny little cubicle of an office in the post office building.

Reb Eliyahu's star witness, Boleslav Mi-kalauskus, had been instructed to meet him in his office early in the morning to go over a few last details of his testimony. When Boli had arrived, he was in the company of his partner-in-crime. The prosecutor firmly advised Vladi to take his place in the spectators' gallery. Reb Eliyahu still did not have a plan, but he knew that, come what may, keeping Boleslav separated from his more intelligent alter-ego would prove essential.

After banishing the uninvited Vladislav, Reb Eliyahu greeted Boleslav warmly, inquiring after his health and that of his family. Boleslav, whose breath clearly indicated his prior consumption of the breakfast of champions, thanked the prose-cutor and began to make a remark about that 'cursed Jew, Moshe Lishinsky' when he caught himself and fell silent. Reb Eliyahu smiled and produced a large, unopened bottle of the most expensive vodka available, praying that, with a little help from the tongue-loosening liquid, Bole-slav might candidly reveal the truth. Boleslav raised the bottle to his lips and downed a quantity that would likely prove lethal to any run-of-the-mill alcoholic.

Reb Eliyahu, opening his office door with a

polite after-you gesture, accompanied Boleslav downstairs to the courtroom. Ever vigilant against contact with Vladislav, he seated his witness at the prosecution table. The entrance of the town's most prominent Jew together with the town's most prominent victim created a stir in the courtroom. The uproar ended abruptly as the Chief of Police, now functioning as bailiff, called the court to order and announced the opening of the proceedings.

THE PROSECUTION had but two witnesses, Boli and Vladi. Kaganoff interrogated them as he had never interrogated before. Boleslav was the first to take the stand, and he testified that he had sold his mare to Lishinsky for a remarkably good price (to use Vladi's words) and had waited thirty days for payment. When none was forthcoming, he had gone to the home of the defendant to collect — only to be ejected bodily from the premises. Vladislav testified next, corroborating the story of the abortive collection attempt.

Try as he might, Reb Eliyahu was unable to shake the two from their story. His attempts to confuse them so that they might contradict each other only had the effect of bringing the judge, a decent and fair-minded man, to ask the prosecutor why he was cross-examining his own witnesses. "Your honor, I am only trying to build an air-tight case for the prosecution."

"Very well, Mr. Kaganoff. Carry on."

But the story was too simple, and Vladislav had rehearsed his partner too well. The cross-examination by the defense was half-hearted at best. A well-meaning Gentile, the lawyer could never hope to equal the courtroom technique of Eliyahu Kaganoff, and Kaganoff himself had already covered all the ground.

Moshe Lishinsky's attorney called several character witnesses, peasants who had worked for Reb Moshe or had dealings with him, and all grudgingly admitted that the defendant had always been honest, fair, and even charitable. Finally, he called Reb Moshe, who gave his account of the transaction, telling how he had naively agreed to pay cash at the seller's request and explaining that receipts were never used in the town since most of the peasants were illiterate. The prosecution did not bother cross-examining any of the witnesses for the defense, and when the judge called a recess for lunch, he instructed the two sides to be ready to present closing arguments when the proceedings resumed.

ELIYAHU KAGANOFF sat with his face in his hands as the courtroom began to empty. "Uh, can I go now, Mr. Kaganoff?" It was Boli. Reb Eliyahu did not look up but gestured dismissively with his hand. "Yes, Boleslav, have some lunch, but be back for the closing arguments."

"Yes, sir, Mr. Kaganoff. We're really going to get that old *Zhi...* uh, uh, Mr. Kaganoff?"

"Yes, Boleslav."

"You know that vodka in your office? You think

there's any left?"

"Yes, yes, Boleslav. Take it with you. Take the whole bottle."

"Thank you, Mr. Kaganoff."

"Of course, Boleslav. Any time," he sighed. "Any time, any place. What's the difference?"

With that Kaganoff sat bolt upright. "Any place!" he thought. If there is any *place* where I can think my way out of this..." Slipping out the rear entrance to the post office building, Reb Eliyahu Kaganoff made his way to his secret retreat, where he had thought his way out of so many tight intellectual spots in the past. The very site of his clandestine rendezvous with Reb Moshe.

Vladi, Boli, and most of the spectators made their way to the tavern for a liquid lunch.

H OW DID I get into this?" Kaganoff asked himself. "I *know* how I got into it. Reb Moshe Lishinsky trusted one of them."

"So why did I ever become State Prosecutor? It's not a job for a Jew!"

"Irrelevant. Stick to the topic."

"So maybe he really is guilty. I used every device I know and couldn't get those two drunks to change their story."

"Nonsense. If Moshe Lishinsky says he paid, he paid. It's as simple as that."

"So *they're* guilty, but how can I show it?"

"What if I don't show it?"

"If I call for the maximum penalty, maybe the mob will be satisfied and leave the rest of us alone. It's his own fault; he never should have been so trusting."

"How could I let Moshe Lishinsky rot in a Hapsburg prison?"

"Lishinsky knows how to take care of himself."

"Who am I kidding? Even if the other prisoners don't finish him off, the conditions will. And worst of all, he's innocent."

"If he's innocent, why don't I just ask for a dismissal? The judge would do as I ask."

"Sure he would, but I'd never get out of the courtroom alive, nor would Moshe. And once they've tasted the blood of two Jews, they won't stop. The life of every Jew in this town would be on my head! I must show those two thieving drunkards for what they are. There is no other way! But how?"

A S KAGANOFF sank ever deeper in thought, running his fingers through his hair and pulling at his beard, the courtroom began to fill. Shortly, the Chief of Police/bailiff called the proceedings to order, but only Boleslav Mikalauskus was seated at the prosecution table, and he was in no state to deliver a closing argument. When the judge extended the recess for another half hour, sausages, cheeses, black bread, herring and snuff appeared from nowhere and were passed around. A few of the braver souls even managed to sneak a few swigs of "the real thing," despite the courtroom ban on alcoholic beverages.

An hour passed, and still no prosecutor. The judge extended the recess indefinitely and remained in his place. A low murmur of conversation filled the courtroom. Boleslav Mikalauskus snored loudly.

The food did not mollify the crowd long enough to prevent the spectators' gallery from being transformed into a symposium on recent developments in inter-ethnic relations. "Where is he, that *Zhid*, may he find his way to an early grave?"

"He's probably out casting a Jewish spell on all of us."

"Or drinking the blood of an innocent Christian."

"The *Zhids* are trying to take over this town and ruin all the upright Christians, but this time that Lishinsky will pay."

Finally, Kaganoff, extremely distraught and disheveled, returned to the courtroom and headed directly for the bench. "I beg your indulgence, your honor, but I *must* confer with Mr. Mikalauskus."

"You have delayed these proceedings enough already!"

"Your honor, I cannot make my closing argument until I have conferred with Mr. Mikalauskus."

"Very well," the judge answered irritably. "But make it brief!"

BOLESLAV," Kaganoff barked, shaking the sleeping peasant by the shoulder, "come with me to my office." The prosecutor hurried Boli to his office and immediately proffered another bottle of vodka. As Boleslav proceeded to upend it, Kaganoff winced and began. "Boleslav! Do you understand me?"

"Yesh, shir."

"Where are we?"

"In your offish."

"Excellent. Now, Boleslav, you know I'm on your side, don't you?"

"Yesh, shir."

"And you know I'm doing all I can to help you and Vladislav."

"Yesh, shir."

"But, Boleslav, my good man, up to now it's been a free ride. Do you understand me?"

"No, shir."

"Boleslav, up to now, I've been helping you for free. Do you get my meaning?"

"Yesh, shir."

"As we both know, that isn't how things are done, now, is it?"

"No, shir."

"All right. Now let me make myself clear. I am the State Prosecutor. Do you understand? Do you know what that means?"

"Yesh, shir."

"It means that I can drop these charges right now, and if I do, Moshe Lishinsky will walk home none the worse for wear. Now, we both know your game, so I want you to tell me: How much is Vladislav Bratkowski getting?"

"He shaid that if the old *Zhid* payzh a shecond time, he getsh half."

"I see. Fine. So here is what we will do. If I see to it that the old Jew pays you double, then I too will receive half of the original price. That's half the original price for me, half for Bratkowski, and you will keep the entire additional payment that is equal to the original price. Do you agree?"

Boli's eyes were getting vacant.

"Do you agree, Boleslav?"

"Yesh."

"Do you have money here? I want my payment as soon as the judge issues his ruling."

"What?"

"Do you have money here?"

"Yesh."

"Show me. Excellent."

Reb Eliyahu dragged Boli back to the court-room, apologized to the judge, and, being extremely careful to avoid the eyes of Reb Moshe Lishinsky, launched into his closing argument.

YOUR HONOR, there is little to argue here. This is a case of fraud, pure and simple. You have heard in testimony how the wealthy Mr. Lishinsky took advantage of the poor, naive Mr. Mikalauskus, how he took advantage of the trust that the good Christians of this community have for the Jews. He betrayed that trust. And for what, your honor? For the price of one mare. What is one mare to Lishinsky, your honor? Here is a man who could afford a hundred mares. Surely he does not deserve your sympathy. Your honor, I ask you to find the defendant guilty as charged.

"As State Prosecutor, your honor, I am obliged not only to prove the guilt of the accused, but also to recommend his punishment. But before I do, allow me, with your honor's gracious permission, to add a personal note. It is no secret that I myself am of the Jewish persuasion. I have always been a proud Jew and deemed it a privilege to be a member of an ancient and honorable people. This community knows that I and the rest of my co-religionists have always dealt honestly with our good Christian neighbors and shown them the utmost respect. This is why our two communities are able to live here in peace and brotherhood.

"But this day, your honor, I am ashamed. Ashamed to be Jewish. And why am I ashamed?

Because of this Lishinsky. Moshe Lishinsky has done what no other Jew in this town, and I believe no other Jew in this country, would dare to do. He has cheated another human being. We Jews stand for honesty in business and have always dealt honestly with our Gentile neighbors.

"Lishinsky, however, has violated not only the trust of the good Christians of this town, he has violated the trust of his own people as well. Every Jew in Kalisz, indeed every Jew in Austro-Hungary, hangs his head in shame today.

"It is for this reason, your honor, that I ask for the maximum penalty prescribed by law. I ask that Lishinsky be compelled to pay double the price of the mare to Boleslav Mikalauskus and in addition, as an example to others, that he receive the maximum prison sentence at hard labor."

This last request elicited an audible gasp of disbelief from Moshe Lishinsky, whose confidence in Kaganoff had already been shaken severely. But before Reb Moshe had time to consider the matter, he heard Reb Eliyahu conclude, "May this serve as a warning to other members of my faith who would violate the sacred trust of their Gentile neighbors. May the kind and devout Christians of this community forgive us this day, and may our two peoples continue to live together in peace and prosperity for many years to come."

Boleslav, tranquilly slobbering in his sleep, jumped as the judge's gavel banged twice. There was no deliberation. The judge ruled immediately. "Lishinsky, Moshe, I sentence you to pay

twice the original price of the mare to Boleslav
Mikalauskus and to serve five years at hard labor."

THE SPECTATORS' GALLERY exploded
with cheering. Bottles were passed openly
now as backs were thumped and hands were
pressed. The crowd seemed satisfied; Kaganoff's
summation, along with the judge's sentence,
seemed to have appeased its lust for Jewish
blood, at least for the present. Even Vladislav
smiled benignly. The Archbishop made his way to
the judge to offer his congratulations on a wise
verdict and inquire after his health.

At the defendant's table, the attorney for the
defense assembled his papers. Next to him,
Moshe Lishinsky sat staring morosely in the direction of the bench, gripping the table for support. Only at the prosecutor's table was the atmosphere cool and business-like; here, money
was about to change hands.

Kaganoff deftly maneuvered his body so as to
block the transaction from the prying eyes
around them and, trying to shield himself from
the vodka fumes, whispered, "Well, Boleslav,
aren't you going to thank me?"

"Thank you, Mishter Kaganoff."

"And what about my, shall we say, fee?"

"What?"

"My fee, my fee. Where's my cut of the take, my
good man?"

"Oh, sure. Jusht a minute." Boli began fumbling

in his pocket. "Here, Mishter Kaganoff. Do you want to count it?"

"Of course I want to count it. You think I'm as stupid as Lishinsky?" At this, even Boli smiled. "Now, let me have a look at those bills." He made a show of examining the notes.

"Look here, Boleslav. Who are you trying to fool? This is counterfeit money!"

"What?"

"This is counterfeit money! These bills are no good!"

"Mishter Kaganoff, shir, therzh nothing wrong with thozh billzh."

"There certainly is. I am a State Prosecutor, and I know counterfeit money when I see it. You're trying to cheat me just as you cheated Lishinsky." Reb Eliyahu was speaking very rapidly in a low whisper, and Boleslav was in no condition to catch every word. "I said you're trying to cheat me, like you cheated Lishinsky."

"No, shir, Mishter Kaganoff, I wouldn't cheat you."

"Oh, no? Then let's take these bills and show them to the judge."

"What?"

"Let's show the money to the judge, I said."

"Sure, Mishter Kaganoff. Whatever you shay."

HIS HONOR and his eminence were still exchanging pleasantries when the State

Prosecutor and his star witness approached them. The Archbishop turned. "Ah, Mr. Kaganoff, a very fine oration that was, very fine indeed. I would like very much to talk to you some time about Christianity."

"Thank you, your eminence, I think that might be very interesting. With your permission, I have an urgent need to speak with you and his honor.

"Your honor, your eminence, Mikalauskus here asked my opinion on these bills and I have advised him that they are counterfeit, but he does not agree. What is your opinion?"

"Let me see them," the judge answered, pulling out his reading glasses. "They look all right to me," he continued, passing them on to the Archbishop who, not being an expert, nodded his assent.

"Your honor, your eminence, I am convinced that they are counterfeit! Look here at the quality of the paper. Look at the smudginess of the ink."

"Oh, come now, Kaganoff, they look perfectly fine to me. We could have them sent to Vienna for analysis, but I hardly think that necessary."

"Nor do I, your honor. I am a State Prosecutor, and I know counterfeit bills when I see them."

"Now Kaganoff, no one is disputing that you are a State Prosecutor and, I concede, a good one at that. That was an outstanding summation you made just a few minutes ago, a credit to your people; but let's not make a tempest in a teapot over a few bills. I'm sure we can get to the bottom of this right now.

"Look here, Mikalauskus," the judge continued, turning to Boleslav, "where did you get these bills?"

Boli had trouble following the conversation conducted in a more refined Polish than he had ever heard in his life. He wiped his mouth with the back of his hand before emitting his usual, "What?"

"Where did you get these bills?"

"I got them from the Jew when he bought my mare, the one with tubercu... tubercu... the one who got shick."

Now it was the judge's turn. "What did you say?"

"I got them from Lishinsky over there, when he bought my mare." Boli stopped for a second, and then suddenly his hand flew to his mouth again, although this time it was not to wipe away the saliva trickling down his chin, but rather to try to recapture his words.

Physically, the middle-aged Eliyahu Kaganoff did not stand a chance against the Polish pig farmer much his junior. Kaganoff was keenly aware of this all along, just as he knew that as soon as Boleslav Mikalauskus figured things out, he would go straight for the State Prosecutor's neck. With the advantage of advanced warning coupled by the fact that Boli's reflexes had been placed at a considerable disadvantage by a colossal quantity of vodka, he was ready when the pair of powerful hands came lunging at him. Kaganoff ducked just in time for Mikalauskus to knock the Archbishop flat on the floor.

It must have taken a good ten minutes of gaveling and shouting to silence the courtroom, restrain Boli, and reopen the trial. It took only another five for the judge, on his own initiative, to sentence Mikalauskus and Bratkowski to the punishment previously prescribed for Reb Moshe Lishinsky.

Heard from: Mr. Ed Heller

Extracurricular Activity

LEAH AND BINA GARFEIN went to school on the side. Like many other residents of Jerusalem's Mattersdorf neighborhood, most of their education took place in the home of Rebbetzin Yehudis Schlessinger. Although her modest apartment was like any other in Mattersdorf, the Rebbetzin herself was one of a kind.

Not only did Rebbetzin Schlessinger have an opinion on every conceivable matter, she possessed voluminous data to support her position. Indeed, as encyclopedic as her mind was, and as deftly as she separated fact from fiction, there was always a faintly mystical sense that whatever she knew, she knew firsthand.

It was the Garfein girls' favorite pastime to approach their esteemed neighbor for insight into the news and views of the past and present. And so it was that one overcast afternoon, braving Jerusalem's iciest winter winds, Leah and Bina hurried toward their mentor's flat, clutching the morning paper. The op-ed section featured a full-page tribute to the benevolent Dutch, who had endangered their lives to shelter their Jewish countrymen during World War II. The editorial had been timed to coincide with the anniversary of the 1941 "February Strike" in Amsterdam.

The strike, the paper reported, had been precipitated by the "Black Sabbath" three days earlier, which marked the first time that Jews were robbed, beaten, and carted off wholesale. During the *aktion,* bloodthirsty stormtroopers and Dutch Nazis together descended upon the Jewish quarter, finding it defenseless but for one courageous Jew, who dared to throw acid in the face of his would-be assassin.

The Germans swiftly meted out a response designed to teach any other potential insurrectionists a cruel lesson. Over four hundred young Jewish men were either kidnapped in the streets or snatched from their homes, whereupon they were forced to kneel on the sidewalks for hours. This was followed by a command performance of Nazi-orchestrated gymnastics, brutal beatings, and deportation.

DUTCH CITIZENS were so outraged by what they had witnessed that they took action: strongly worded pamphlets were distributed, and bicyclists passed the word urging a one-day strike to protest the maltreatment of Jews.

On February 25th, the citizens of Amsterdam followed the lead of their streetcar and sanitation workers and walked off the job. The usually bustling metropolis was virtually paralyzed as shops closed, factories shut down, offices emptied, and newspapers went unpublished. The shipyards were deserted and the streets were still.

Furious at this mass concession to conscience, the Nazis ordered work to resume, but instead the strike spread further to Hilversum, Haarlem, and Zaandam.

Leah and Bina were aware of the Dutch reputation for compassion during the war, but they had known nothing of this kind of national solidarity. Since Rebbetzin Schlessinger was born in Europe, they were eager to hear her incisive commentary.

T HE LOCAL FOUNT of information escorted her two young guests into the living room, donned her reading glasses, and read aloud from the newspaper column:

> The members of the Dutch Underground acted like model citizens, enabling them to fight the Nazis in secret. The Underground hid Jews in homes throughout Holland and provided them with forged identity cards, which were used to secure food rations.
>
> There is ample testimony of the many noble deeds per-

formed by warm hosts who shared what meager food and clothing they had. Some took little or nothing for room and board and rebuffed offers of compensation by saying, "We'll talk about that when the war is over." One Dutchman proved so adept at hiding Jews that when seventeen German policemen raided his farm for five hours, they found nothing. They knew that he was harboring Jews, however, so they threatened to raze every building to the ground unless he handed over the fugitives the next day. Accordingly, the Jews resolved to leave that very night but their host wouldn't hear of it. "God is with us today," he insisted, "and He will not desert us tomorrow." And indeed, every one of those Jews survived the war.

The Rebbetzin seemed transfixed by the article. And then, in a most uncharacteristic fit of rage, she flung the paper down on the table. "I see," she said evenly, slowly regaining her composure, "that today is the day we are to celebrate the benevolent Dutch, the humanitarians of history... Well, it is time to set the record straight."

LEAH AND BINA knew that they were in for an enlightening session, and they edged their chairs closer in anticipation. "My dear girls," Rebbetzin Schlessinger began, "the facts of the period have been widely distorted. Let me provide you with some sobering statistics:

"It is a matter of record that eighty-five percent of Holland's Jewish population was exterminated by the Nazis — proportionally more than in any other Nazi-occupied country except Poland. Not coincidentally, the gas chambers in Auschwitz were manned by Dutch volunteers. Holland, my dears, was not the haven people imagine it was!

"Furthermore, once the Netherlands government was exiled to London during the war, it closed its eyes to the fate of Dutch Jewry. And the Red Cross, supposedly such a compassionate and humanitarian organization, did nothing for the Jews languishing in camps on Dutch soil."

"You can't really expect the Red Cross to have intervened in camps run by the Nazis!" Bina interrupted.

"You have forgotten," Rebbetzin Schlessinger was quick to remind her, "that Jews were not the Nazis' only enemies. Communists and other political prisoners also were banished to the camps. They, too, were either worked to death or killed outright. But — and this is a very big 'but' — the Red Cross did intercede on their behalf, and so did the Church.

I N SHORT," the Rebbetzin told her youthful protégées, "the rescue efforts carried out by the Dutch have been exaggerated. I realize that when people are bent on your destruction and all your neighbors are either aiding and abetting the genocide or standing idly by, it is only natural to hope for support. And I cannot deny that the February Strike was a remarkable act of courage and brotherhood. But the fact is that the Dutch had plenty of other opportunities to help the Jews — both directly and indirectly, and without risk to themselves — but they neglected to take advantage of them."

The two sisters gawked at Rebbetzin Yehudis, their eyes pleading her to tell more. No pleading was required, however; she was already locked into her pedagogic mode and she had no intention of cutting the lesson short.

"Aside from the Dutch Nazis, thousands of 'upstanding' Netherlanders enthusiastically collaborated with the Germans — from the Dutch police who arrested Jews, to the opportunists who took money to smuggle their fellow citizens out of the country and then betrayed them. Many looted Jewish homes as soon as the residents were deported, and just as many promised to safeguard the deportees' possessions but refused to return them to the survivors after the war. And a great many of those who hid Jews did so only for exorbitant fees."

The girls looked at one another in dismay. "But didn't a lot of people take in Jewish children?" Leah asked.

"Yes, they certainly did. It has been said that they were decent, compassionate people who undertook great risks to save innocent boys and girls."

Leah and Bina nodded, indicating that they were indeed familiar with this historical account.

"Some of the people who sheltered children were as selfless as a human can be, but I must inform you, they were the minority. The overwhelming majority sheltered Jewish children either with the intention of converting them to Christianity, or because they themselves were barren and wanted children of their own — even Jewish ones, if need be."

One by one, the girls' illusions were being shattered. They couldn't help but be skeptical.

"I SEE YOU DON'T believe me," Rebbetzin Schlessinger said. She excused herself for a moment while she rummaged through the file cabinets in her study. "Ah, here we are," she announced, brandishing a yellowed document. "Before the liberation, the Dutch Ministry of Justice and representatives of the Resistance groups drafted a bill to determine the future of all the Jewish youngsters. It was a very unusual bill, as you will soon see, unusual because the attitude it reveals is so completely at odds with what you and very many others always believed to be true.

"First, according to this document, it is most apparent that the children's natural parents were not expected to return. Second, the children were considered *abandoned* or *neglected,* not orphaned. Thus, the bill implies that the tie that customarily exists between child and family in these instances *warranted* severing. The third point is that the Resistance legally took precedence in deciding the children's fate, whereas their relatives were regarded as meddlesome outsiders. In fact, parents were often denied all contact with their children, yet forced to pay child support. Shall I go on?"

Leah discerned immediately the sinister intent behind the bill the Ministry of Justice had sanctioned. Bina, however, found it hard to believe that the Resistance groups which had fought so valiantly to maintain freedom would so wantonly usurp the liberty of stranded Jewish children. Needless to say the girls nodded for Rebbetzin Schlessinger to continue.

"Good. Fourth, the Commission for War Foster Children was directed by former Resistance fighters. According to the document, its members were committed to improving Dutch society by 'eradicating racism and divisive denominational differences.' So Jewish survivors who demanded custody of their relatives were regarded as ingrates and obstacles to social progress! The document deemed it fitting that those who had saved the lives of thousands should be empowered to *shape* those very lives! And as for the children themselves, if any refused to convert to Christianity, they were considered disloyal and ungrateful.

"And finally, the bill refused to recognize Judaism as a factor in the children's future. Do you understand?" the Rebbetzin asked, slowing her cadence and softening her voice. "In its stubborn, sanctimonious blindness to religious and ethnic differences, the commission was actually guilty of discrimination!"

Rebbetzin Schlessinger paused a final time to make sure that Leah and Bina had grasped the diabolical scheme engineered by the host families. This wasn't the kind of insight they had expected to glean from their lesson.

"In other words," Rebbetzin Yehudis emphasized, "as the war neared its end, the Resistance foresaw an unpleasant confrontation between its members and the Jewish survivors. So to protect their interests, the Resistance leaders drafted this insidious legislation! Now, now," she said, holding up her hand to forestall the girls' arguments. "Since I see that you are not impressed with the facts, I am going to tell you a story. I want you to listen very carefully, for every word of it is true."

BY THE TIME the Nazis and their Dutch collaborators had commenced their *aktions* and deportations in the winter of 1943," Rebbetzin Yehudis began, "Jews had long been forbidden to use public or private transportation or to enter public areas; eventually they were even forbidden to leave their homes. Clandestine activities became the order of the day, and thousands of Jews went into hiding, among them a little girl named Jenny.

"Word reached Jenny's mother that Jenny's escape contact was en route to their house, so she bid a hasty farewell to her delicate five-year-old daughter, knowing she probably would never see her again. Jenny's father had already been turned over to the Gestapo by the Dutch police.

"On the way to Freisland, in northern Holland, the Underground first concealed and later disguised the little girl. As it was too dangerous to hide several family members at any one address, and inadvisable for all of them to try to escape together, Jenny's younger sister would undergo a similar excursion the next day, with a different destination. Her baby brother's transport, in contrast, was coordinated by the Nazis, and he accompanied his mother all the way to Auschwitz.

AS YOU MIGHT imagine, it was difficult for Jenny to adjust to living with foster parents in provincial, Protestant Freisland. But by the time she had finally started to feel somewhat at home there, a neighbor betrayed her and she had to flee.

"Eventually she was able to return to her foster home but the reunion was short-lived: an Underground member who had infiltrated the local Nazi hierarchy informed her adopted family that she had again been discovered. With no time to spare or despair, the young waif was dispatched to a farm community, making her way back to Freisland only several months later. From the time she returned until the end of the war, she never again ventured outside, although she posed as a Gentile girl whose natural parents had been killed by a bomb blast.

"Jenny's foster parents were kind, good-hearted people. Their Underground participation made their home a hub of activities and a target for their enemies. One day, as her 'father' sat peeling potatoes with Jenny at his side, a German soldier, accompanied by a rifle-wielding band of local Nazis, broke into the house. Possessed of nerves of steel, the father did not even look up from his work.

"'Hands up!' came the order, punctuated by a sharp jab from a rifle muzzle.

"Refusing to be cowed, the father spat at the Nazi's boots.

"Jenny began to tremble with fear, and her

heart was pounding so that she felt it would burst out of her tiny chest. Her foster father was quite a catch since he could identify all the Resistance members and he knew where all the arms were stashed throughout Freisland. For the time being, it was only he they were after.

"Little did the Nazis realize that Jenny was just as knowledgeable. As the Underground's 'mascot,' she attended every one of their meetings. She also had the distinguished honor of beginning the proceedings by hooking up the radio wires that connected the assembled — however fleetingly — to the outside world. You see, listening to the BBC or the Underground Voice of Orange, even owning a radio, was against the conquerors' law."

But it was not Jenny's wartime exploits that Rebbetzin Schlessinger wished to recount to her spellbound audience. Every Jewish child who went into hiding had a riveting tale to tell. Every boy and girl experienced the same ever-present fear of the enemy and dread of betrayal. And every one of them subsisted on the most meager rations, lived in dark, cramped quarters, and was always on the move. What was unique about Jenny's story was what happened after the war.

J ENNY'S war-ravaged uncle survived the Holocaust," the Rebbetzin resumed. "After a grueling trip by foot and by bicycle, he arrived in Freisland, half-dead but determined to regain custody of his beloved niece, who shared his last name. His efforts, however, were in vain.

"Jenny was somewhat prepared for this tragic

turn of events, for even during the war any talk of her being reunited with her family had been taboo. And as soon as the war was over, her foster parents registered her under *their* name in their passports.

"Life grew increasingly traumatic for this lonely eight-year-old girl who had no idea if her real parents or siblings were still alive. She was under constant pressure to become a good Christian, and both her foster family and her community perpetually reminded her that whoever did not affirm his faith in the 'Savior' would be condemned to perdition.

"In their zeal to 'save' her," the Rebbetzin pointed out, "they provided her with more religious training than others her age received. No effort was spared to ensure her a Christian future and to discredit her Jewish past. In fact, whenever Jenny did something wrong, it was supposedly the Jew within her that had led her astray.

S UCH TORMENT rent Jenny's tender soul, but she instinctively stood up for her people. 'I just happen to be mischievous,' she would insist. 'It has nothing to do with the Jews.' A meaningless defense to the Freislanders.

"Every week Jenny was subjected to fire-and-brimstone sermons in church and at school, where she was the lone Jewish pupil. Yet, paradoxically, the more she was branded a product of an 'evil doctrine,' the more she grew curious about her own heritage — and contemptuous of Christianity.

"As a result, Jenny felt more isolated than ever. She could not broach the subject with her foster parents, simple people who would never have understood her doubts, and most probably would have resented them. Nor could she unburden herself to the local clergy, who were committed to molding her into a model Christian.

"To make matters worse, her theological dilemma gave rise to emotional insecurity. Since she was unmistakably different from her Gentile peers, she began to wonder if she was normal. Her classmates and her foster family began to wonder the same thing, as Jenny refused to fraternize with her contemporaries or date the local boys, even though she had no idea if there were any Jewish boys left to marry.

"After the war, a task force of Jewish social workers partially allayed her worries. Commissioned by the *Ezrat Hayeled* umbrella organization, the social workers were assigned the job of interviewing Jewish orphans each year and reporting on their development. The responses they received were invariably less than accurate. The foster families were always given enough advance notice before the official yearly visit, so that they were able to prime their wards to relate how 'wonderful' life was away from their natural family and that they never wished to leave.

"When Jenny, who had come from a devout, Orthodox family, was first approached by one of the thoroughly secular, Jewish social workers, she was ecstatic to learn that there were other Jews still alive, although what she saw was distinctly different from what she remembered of her people. 'Aren't there any other Jews?' she pressed.

"At the invitation of *Ezrat Hayeled*, Jenny vacationed in Amsterdam, where she could see for herself some of the Jewish survivors. This brief visit developed into an annual event, and one year Jenny wistfully told her sponsors that she had never set foot inside a synagogue.

"*Ezrat Hayeled* was quick to honor her implicit request by arranging a stop at the Reform congregation. Since the Rabbi of the temple happened to have come from an observant family and had attended the very same yeshivah as Jenny's father, he welcomed her warmly into his temple and introduced her to his brand of Judaism.

"The Rabbi did not win himself a 'convert' but he did strengthen Jenny's conviction that Freisland was not her home and never could be. Aching to leave the community but reluctant to hurt her foster parents, the frustrated young girl bided her time, sensing that her Hebrew studies in the local school would someday prove more practical than her minister-teachers ever imagined.

WHEN JENNY reached college age, she finally had an excuse to pack her bags: with no institutes of higher learning in Freisland, and with a generous loan from *Ezrat Hayeled*, she was off to Amsterdam. Knowing instinctively that there had to be more to Judaism than what she had witnessed at the Reform temple, she pleaded with her sponsors to let her board with an observant family, but they refused.

"In all their years of dealing with orphans with a host of emotional problems and special demands, the *Ezrat Hayeled* officials had never encountered anyone as stubborn as Jenny. In the end, remarkably enough, she wore them down and they arranged for her to stay with the Bnei Akiva *shaliach* from Israel.

"Jenny's new hosts had no idea why she was so eager to lodge with a religious family for she knew nothing about Judaism. Even Yom Kippur was foreign to her. Yet they obligingly answered all her questions and explained the complexities of Jewish law. They also provided her with religious literature in Hebrew — her language studies were paying off at last.

JENNY'S GREATEST joy came the first day she attended services at what remained of the Orthodox synagogue in Amsterdam. Even though she had spent her life attending church, and even though the Reform temple was more like what she was used to, she felt completely at home in the *shul*.

"Ironically, thirteen years after the Germans surrendered, the war was finally over for her. With a *siddur* in her hand and a lump in her throat, she suddenly realized that she had nothing to fear anymore, and nothing to hide.

"Her Jewish education was just beginning, however, so college was placed on the back burner. After a year, Jenny's hosts returned to Israel and pleaded with her to join them, but she felt unworthy of settling in the Holy Land until she knew more about Judaism.

"During Jenny's second year in Amsterdam, she began to study with graduates of the Gateshead teachers' seminary. But despite these inspiring tutorials, constant invitations from religious families, and all the other trappings of religious life in Amsterdam, Jenny felt somehow incomplete. It wasn't until *Simchas Torah* that she realized what she was missing.

"Watching the frail old men of Amsterdam fervently reciting the festive prayers and circling the *sefer Torah* with quiet dignity and joy, a stark realization overcame her: If she didn't devote herself to full-time Jewish study immediately, it would be too late to ever catch up.

"Jenny therefore applied to *Ezrat Hayeled* to sponsor her transfer from Amsterdam University to Gateshead.

I T WAS twenty years before the *baal teshuvah* movement," Rebbetzin Schlessinger reminded Leah and Bina, "and *Ezrat Hayeled* was aghast at Jenny's aspirations. 'For Heaven's sake, you must not study Judaism!' the organization insisted. 'We are willing to support your becoming an actress, a dancer, or even a kibbutznik, but Judaism is out!'

"With the tenacity of a lifelong fighter, Jenny lobbied the executive of *Ezrat Hayeled* — to no avail. So once again she had to bide her time until she would reach majority and legal independence. Indeed, on her twenty-first birthday, she bid farewell to her sponsors in Amsterdam and her foster family in Freisland — who made her feel like a criminal for rejecting Christianity — and prepared to sail for England.

"One hitch Jenny had not anticipated was her rejection from Gateshead on the grounds that she was too old (the average student age at the time was sixteen). Yet once in London, she galvanized support and, with characteristic determination, was eventually admitted.

"Considering Jenny's anti-Jewish upbringing, it is a miracle that she ended up marrying a Jew. Her sister was not as fortunate, nor were ninety-nine percent of the orphans sheltered during the war. After all, their only hope of exposure to Judaism was via a Jewish organization bent on assimilation. Furthermore, the post-war rehabilitation of children focused on those who had experienced the horrors of the camps, while those who had not were presumed untraumatized and therefore were either ignored or afforded secondary importance."

L EAH AND BINA Garfein's heads were spinning with images of Jenny's unforgettable odyssey. Her against-all-odds escape at age five, her years of hiding, her struggle to be Jewish — it was absolutely mind-boggling! But Rebbetzin Schlessinger still had one more bombshell for them.

"I'm sure you must be wondering how I could know all these intimate details about a Jewish war orphan. Well, girls," she concluded with a small, wistful smile, "it's really quite simple: that little Jenny was me."

Heard from: "Rebbetzin Schlessinger"

In Sickness
and in Health

THERE HAVE been many famous couples throughout Jewish history. Dozens of names come to mind; but foremost among them are surely Zish Gutnick and his second wife, Briendel.

WHAT? You mean to say you've never heard of Zish Gutnick and his second wife Briendel? Let me introduce you.

Zish Gutnick was a survivor of the Great War. As a young war orphan, he was shoved, along with scores of other Jews from war-ravaged Rumania, down the hold of a smelly, leaking tanker, and together they bobbed and rolled their way over the ocean to Palestine. The trip from Rumania to the Holy Land was the worst and best trip of Zish's life. He was seasick and cold and thirsty, excited and happy and joyous, scared and full of hope and confidence — all at the same time. When the long voyage was finally over on a moonless night in the summer of 1921, Zish and 83 of his compatriots waded ashore to live as Jews in the land of their forefathers.

Zish was welcomed by a family and raised on what was the first attempt at a religious *moshav*. School was out of the question (the *moshav* didn't have one), so Zish spent his youth bouncing around from one job to another. After some years, it became apparent that *moshav* life wasn't for him. What was for him, no one knew. Unfortunately, the notion of vocational counseling hadn't been thought of yet. So Zish left the *moshav* and went to Jerusalem to live with a distant relative.

IN JERUSALEM, Zish got a job as a handy-man, a misnomer if ever there was one. And if ever there was a man who shouldn't have been trusted with tools, it was Zish. It wasn't that he was incompetent. No, if he fixed a roof, it usually stayed fixed — at least until he got paid. It was just that tools and Zish appeared to be mortal enemies. If he had a hammer, he would smash any nail in sight, especially his fingernails. A saw was an invitation to perform the ancient medical practice of blood-letting. His face, hands, arms, legs and back were always finding new ways to get beaten and bruised.

And behind every bruise, there was a story; if

Zish was working on top of a building, there were usually two or three stories. How many times he actually fell off one was anybody's guess. Even Zish had lost count. Several times he'd also lost consciousness. But a little shpritz of water or a shot of whiskey ("Dat's de only kinda shots I take") was usually all he needed to find it again.

When Zish was an *alte bochur* of 45, he married Zelda. She was 46, the first of five sisters to get born and the last to get married. It wasn't that she hadn't tried; it was just that she had never found the right person. Zish came closer than anyone, and by the time he came around, that was close enough.

For twenty-three years, Zish and Zelda had an ideal partnership. Whatever part of his body he would fracture, break, puncture, cut, bruise, crack, abrade, tear, chip, sever, smash or split, his devoted wife would bandage, salve, disinfect and heal.

It's one of life's ironies that, although Zish spent so much time with one foot in the grave, Zelda was the one who put both feet in first. Maybe all those broken bones broke her spirit. Perhaps she just got sick of playing Florence Nightingale. Whatever the reason, she left life to the living, and at the age of 68 Zish found himself living alone.

"*Oy!*" he said to the mirror. "Do I feel bad! Mein bones ache!"

The mirror did not respond. It just stared back at him. Still, Zish got the message. "*Oy!*" he groaned again as he noticed his reflection. "I look even vorse dan I feel!"

Zish made himself a glass of tea to relax before going to bed. As he sat down at the kitchen table to drink it, he automatically looked for his wife. All he saw was an empty seat. "Zelda, Zelda," he called out, "I'm a sick man! How am I gonna take care of myself? I don't eat. I don't sleep. Vhat's gonna become of me? If you don't vatch over me, pretty soon, you'll haf company!"

T HE NEXT MORNING, Zish miraculously knew what to do. "Vhy didn't I tink of it before? I'll find for me a younk vife. Somevone who can cook and clean. Somevone who can sew and mend. Somevone who can vash mein clodes."

Zish went to *shul* a changed man. As he laid his *tallis* bag on the table, he turned to his geriatric friend of long standing, "Zelig, I gotta get married. Find for me a younk vife."

Zelig was used to Zish's complaints. But this time, it sounded like he was truly serious. "Zish, did you fall off a building again and hurt your head?"

"No. It's like dis: I can barely get up in de mornink. Mein arms is bodderink me. Mein back is killink me. Mein head is achink me. Dat's vhy I need a vife."

"Zish, you don't need a wife. You need a chiropractor."

"I got vone. He don't help. I'm tellink you, I need

a vife, like my Zelda. Only younk. Maybe tirty-sometink."

"Thirty-something? You mean *1930* some-thing! Look, Zish, do yourself a favor. Forget about getting married to anyone. Believe me, you'll be happier."

Zish was insistent. "If you can't help me, I'm gonna find somevone who vill!"

THAT EVENING, on his way home from work, Zish made an unscheduled stop. He dragged his broken body and his heavy tool box up four flights of steps and knocked on the door. The sign on the mailbox downstairs read:

> *MIRIAM GOLDWASSER, SHADCHAN*

"I sure hope so!" Zish said to himself. "Four flights of stairs shouldn't be for notink!"

Before he had a chance to catch his breath or in any other way prepare himself, a silver-haired lady came to the door. By her elegant appearance, refined manner and fancy jewelry, Zish figured he had the right person. "Goot evenink."

"I'm sorry," the lady said, "but I didn't call a carpenter."

"No, you didn't call me. I'm callink you. I'm lookink for mein vife."

"Why, I haven't seen her."

"Either did I since she dite. Dat's vhy I'm here. I need a new vone!"

Miriam Goldwasser smiled in spite of herself. "Come in. What did you say your name is?"

"I didn't. Gutnick. Zish Gutnick. Tenk you."

FOR THE NEXT forty minutes, Zish gave the *shadchan* a rundown on every time he had been run over. When he was finally finished, so was she. "Mr. Gutnick, I really feel for you."

"So you'll marry me?"

Miriam was accustomed to many things, but Zish's straight-ahead approach wasn't one of them. Her poise exploded in a paroxysm of coughing at the very thought.

"No! No! I-I mean you're very nice..."

Seeing how choked-up she'd gotten, Zish was encouraged. "Is dat a yes?" he asked.

"Please, Mr. Gutnick."

"Call me Zish!"

"Zish, I'm flattered. I really am. But I don't think we were made for each other."

"Vhy not?"

"Well, I don't know the first thing about first aid!"

"You could learn. Zelda did."

"Mr. Gutnick..."

"Call me Zish!"

"Mr. Gutnick!"

"Vhat?"

"Listen to me. I am not interested in marrying you. And I don't know of anyone who would be interested in marrying you! Is that clear?"

"Vhen do you tink you'll find somevone? By next veek maybe? I'm not gettink any younker, you know."

"Believe me, I can tell," Miriam said curtly. Then she softened. "My advice to you, Mr. Gutnick, is to check the newspapers."

"I'm not lookink to buy a car."

"No, I mean the personal section. Perhaps you could find someone who would be compatible. In the meantime, if I hear of anyone, I'll let you know."

ZISH WANTED to pursue the matter further, but Miriam politely though firmly showed him the door. Slowly, he descended the four flights of stairs and walked out into the cool Jerusalem breeze.

Down but not out, Zish found himself near a newsstand. "Buy a paper!" he harumphed to himself. "Vhat kind of advice is dat?"

Still, it was the only advice he had. So Zish plunked down a couple of coins for a copy of the evening paper. Impatiently, he scanned the headlines. "Inflation. Crime. Politics. Bah! Dere's notink here for me!"

Still, he kept on reading. Finally, he found the personal column. His eyes grew wide as he studied the ads.

"Seeking a fun-loving, sports-minded, athletic type to work out together."

"I doubt she vould go for roof climbink."

"Elementary school graduate wishing to wed simple woman without intellectual pursuits or aspirations."

"Wrong gender — I tink!"

"Champion swimmer seeks lifesaver."

"Dey can bot jump in de lake togedder."

"Female, Orth. 22, looking for Yeshivish type. No smokers."

"Too younk," he said to himself.

The next ad caught his attention. *"Modern Orthodox woman, mature but young at heart, seeks similar. Obj: matrimony! Write Box 543."*

"Binko! Dat's more like it!" Zish said enthusiastically. He ripped the ad out and stuffed it in his pocket. At home, he searched frantically for a sheet of paper, but all he could find were estimate forms he once had made up. On the back of one of them, in his best penmanship, he scrawled this note:

קמ״ר

Dear Box 543,
    I am self employed
Vidver looking to
remarry.
If interested call dis
number.
            Zish Gutnick

FOR THE NEXT WEEK, Zish jumped every time the phone rang. This was not easy, since he had broken both his legs on several occasions and they screamed in outrage and pain whenever he asked them to function. Furthermore, his body was one big arthritic creak of joints in need of oil.

After ten days of calisthenics, however, his note — and his prayers — were answered.

"Hello?" a warm feminine voice asked quietly. "Is this Mr. Zish Gutnick?"

"Yeah," Zish said, hoping his pounding heart wasn't audible on the other end of the line.

"My name is Briendel Kranovsky. I placed the ad in the newspaper."

"I know," Zish said.

"You know?" Briendel asked, taken aback.

"I mean, I don't know you. I know about de ad."

"Oh, I, uh, understand. Well, I'm not sure where to begin. You see, I've never done anything like this before. But my first husband passed away and I..."

"My first vife pessed avay, too! Vhat a coincidence!" an exuberant Zish interjected.

"I'm not sure," Briendel said hesitantly. "Maybe we could meet someplace and talk?"

"Sure," Zish said in a confident tone. "How bout de Central Bus Station? It's easy to get to. Vhat if I'm meetink you dere tomorrow afternoon, say two o'clock?"

"That sounds fine."

ZISH HUNG UP THE PHONE a new person. He quickly pulled out his *yuntifdikka* suit and tried it on, just to see how he looked. "Not bad," he told himself.

It was only later that night that a frightening thought struck him. He didn't have the slightest idea what she looked like! Zish tried to make a mental picture of the person behind the voice. "I vould say younk. Must be maybe forty-fifty. Nice lookink. I'll know her vhen I see her," he decided finally, and blissfully drifted off to sleep.

By 10 AM, Zish had showered three times. He had also dressed and re-dressed himself, trying every shirt he had with his suit. He made himself a glass of tea to calm down, but was too nervous to drink it. His heart was pounding and that made his legs ache. His bursitis was acting up in his shoulder, so he couldn't lift his arm above his head. His left hand was still bandaged after losing a battle with a hacksaw. Still, Zish felt terrific. By one o'clock, he couldn't stand the tension anymore, and departed for the Central Bus Station.

IF YOU'VE EVER been to Jerusalem's Central Bus Station, you know that it's the *last* place in the world you would want to find or meet anyone! Crowded, noisy, chaotic, it's the city's hub of activity and at any given moment you can see hundreds, if not thousands, of citizens, soldiers, students, street vendors, tourists, taxi drivers, beggars, bus drivers, policemen and others milling around. As soon as Zish entered the center of the confusion which also serves as a lobby, he knew he had made a mistake.

"How am I ever goink to find Briendel in dis place?" he asked himself. There was only one thing to do: Start asking.

"Excuse me," Zish innocently inquired of a tall girl who must have been all of twenty-two years old, "did I talk to you on de phone de odder night maybe?"

"You get out of here!" she quickly replied. "Or I'll notify the authorities!"

Zish tried again. This time, he picked on a raven-haired lady. "Excuse me, by any chance are you lookink for a husband?"

"No!" she said definitively. "And especially not you!"

Zish was used to a lot in his life, but he wasn't used to this. In seconds, his self-confidence was shattered. He beat a hasty retreat to a remote corner of the bus station. "Dis is much harder dan I tought," he muttered.

AFTER CONSIDERING THE MATTER for a few minutes, Zish came up with another plan of attack. "She's obviously lookink for me, so all I gotta do is let her find *me*!" At this, he began to stare meaningfully at every eligible-looking female in the bus station.

Unfortunately, this approach did not have the desired effect. If anything, it was even worse! One young woman was so offended at a steady gaze from a 70-year-old (even if he was a kindly-looking 70-year-old) that she brought a cop over and pointed at Zish accusingly. "That's the one, officer!" she said in a shrill voice.

The policeman told Zish to behave himself.

"Dis is too much!" Zish said, throwing his hands up (until they creaked) in despair. "How can I marry Briendel if I can't even meet her?" Still, his determination was so great that Zish tried again. Only this time, he began to make his way slowly through the moving throngs asking young and old alike, "Briendel? Are you Briendel? Briendel?"

MEANWHILE, Briendel was having troubles of her own. When she had spoken to Zish on the phone, she had thought that it might be hard to find him in a crowd. But he had sounded so self-assured that she didn't have the courage to ask him what he looked like. Now she realized what a mistake it had been to agree to meet at the bus station, and she too was moving slowly through the crowd asking all the men, "Zish? Are you Zish? Zish?" Their responses ranged from a polite "*Gesundheit!*" to something less polite.

Finally, Briendel asked, "Zish?" as Zish posed, "Briendel?"

Zish was the first to react. "Briendel? Is it really you?"

"I-I-I think so. Are you Zish?"

"Yeah. Let's get outta here. I don't wanna attract any more attention."

Briendel and Zish shuffled over to a restaurant. Zish desperately wanted a shot of whiskey to calm his nerves, but he settled for a seltzer. Briendel countered with a glass of tomato juice.

I N THE QUAINT ATMOSPHERE of Sami's Snackiya, Zish studied his mail-order bride. He had memorized the personal column ad by reading it 2,486 times (at last count). Now he compared it with the real thing. She was a good deal older than he had imagined. Instead of a woman in her early forties, she was a grandmotherly matron in her late sixties. In fact, she looked like everybody's *Bubbe*, from her bifocals down to her orthopedic shoes.

Slowly, formally at first, they began to talk and to compare notes. The two hours that they sat in the restaurant seemed to both of them like two minutes. At the end, Zish offered to take her home by cab. As they walked to the street, he noticed for the first time that she limped. "Is your leg okay?" he asked.

"I think so. My knees aren't what they once were."

"So whose are? I got de same problem."

They waited in the shade of a tree for a taxi to pass by. Briendel took a little bottle of pills out of her purse.

"Vhat are dose?"

"The dose the doctor said, a couple liver pills a day. Nothing serious. In fact, except for a few minor aches and pains, I'm as fit as a fiddle." Zish beamed at his good fortune. Briendel just smiled shyly.

THAT'S HOW IT STARTED. Zish courted Briendel for three weeks and then they became man and wife according to the Law of Moses and the State of Israel. For five years, Zish and Briendel lived in harmony. They walked, talked, ate and popped pills together. They became so close that it was soon hard to tell them apart.

"Briendel, mein back," he would *krechtz*.

"Zish, your back, my feet!" she would reply.

"Briendel, mein *kop*!" he would groan.

"Zish, your *kop*, my gall bladder!" she would moan.

And so it went on, one "*krenk* call" after another. For every "*Oy!*" of Zish's, Briendel had an "*Ai!*"

EVENTUALLY, Zish had had enough. "Briendel," he said one night as they met in the kitchen to toast each other with tall, cool glasses of Milk of Magnesia, "we made a mistake. I shoulda found a younker voman and you shoulda found a younker man."

"Now you tell me?"

"*Oy*, Briendel, mein *kishkes*. Listen, maybe it's

not too late. You're in better shape dan I am. It vould be easy for you to find a *shidduch*, some-vone who could take care of you."

"*Ai*, Zish, my arthritis. You might be right. But what about you?"

"I'll see vhat I can find. Maybe I could get a younker voman to take care of me too." Zish looked at his beloved Briendel. This was not the way he had planned things, but what could he do? It was obviously God's Will that they find new partners.

After a minute's silence, he asked, "Vhat do you tink, Briendel? Tell me de trut."

"The truth? Zish, the truth is I'll do whatever makes you happy. But are you sure?"

"I vas right vhen I decided ve should get married, no?"

"Well, yes."

"So I'm right vhen I decide ve should get a divorce!"

T HE NEXT DAY, Zish called a *Beis Din*. He explained the situation over the phone — how he and his wife needed a divorce. Between her low blood sugar and his high blood pressure, they were obviously incompatible. He was told to gather as much documentation as he could and appear with Briendel the following Wednesday.

The week went by much too quickly for both of them. Zish was still working and self-destructing bit by bit. Cut hands, banged-up shins, a strained back. After fifty years of accidents and pain, you'd think his body parts would have learned to get out of the way, but they never cooperated. Whenever something happened, Briendel was there to patch him up.

Unfortunately, the strain of their impending divorce was beginning to tell. They found themselves snapping at each other, they even argued, and once they actually went to sleep without their companionable Milk of Magnesia cocktails.

By the time "D-Day" arrived, they both felt as though they were airsick without ever having left the ground. While Zish went to see the Rabbis, Briendel went to see her doctor. It was just as well; Zish didn't really want her around when he made his big speech.

The Rabbinical court convened promptly at ten. At ten-oh-five, Zish began. "Honored Rabbis," he declared, borrowing a term he had heard used during the *divrei Torah* at *chassunahs*, "I am a poor but honest man. All my life I haf vorked very hard. And I can tell you I haf a lot to show for it — see dis scar? Dat's vhere I fell offa ladder. And dis arm? It vas broken tree times and fixed tvice. And I got more bruises dan de tomatoes on my old *moshav*. And my back, I can't even remember how many times I trew it out. Even my knuckles, dey don't crack no more. Dey just groan."

FOR THE NEXT thirty-five minutes, Zish filled them in on every ache and pain of his existence. After describing a particularly gory encounter with a circular saw, Zish watched the

Rabbis nodding their heads compassionately. It was obvious to him, and to them, that he needed someone who could take better care of him than he could himself. To add weight to his case, Zish brought in notes from doctors and friends testifying to both his honesty and his klutziness. He related his entire medical and personal history in minute detail while the Rabbis took turns dozing. He was just getting to the part where he met Briendel, when she walked in.

"Briendel! Are you okay?" he asked, interrupting himself. "Vhat did de doctor say?"

Briendel looked at the *Beis Din* and tried to force a thin smile of a greeting, but she felt too weak. "*Ai!*" she groaned.

Zish responded with an "*Oy*" of his own and sped to her side. "Briendel, look at you," he cried. "I bet you forgot to take your liver pills again! Here, I'll get you a *glezl vasser*."

Zish excused himself and left the room. He returned with a paper cup filled with warm, cloudy water. "Drink dis," he ordered his soon-to-be exwife. "Now, vhere vere ve? Oh yeah, I first met my vife at the Central Bus — "

"Zish, did you wear your back brace? You know you're not supposed to leave home without it," Briendel interjected.

"Yeah, yeah. I knew you vere goink to ask. So I put it on. And I took mein blood pressure medicine too. Back to the bus station... Oh, I just remembered sometink — Briendel, vhen ve get de divorce, de first tink you haf to do is to promise me

— and I mean *promise* me — you'll check your sugar tvice a day. You know I von't be around to remind you."

"I promise, but only if you'll check your pressure twice a day too. Salt herring isn't good for a man in your condition! And you have to find someone who can make *kishke* like I make."

"I'll try. But let's get back to — "

"Zish!"

"Yeah?"

"Your back! Who's gonna rub your back? You know you can't get out of bed in the morning unless someone rubs your back."

"*Oy*, mein aching back! I forgot all about it. I guess I'll haf to get used to de pain, but de tink dat really vorries me is your dizzy spells. Did you ask de doctor about dem?"

"Yes, he thinks they have something to do with either my heart or my eyeglasses, he's not sure which."

"Right after de divorce, you're gonna haf both checked. You see, your honors?" Zish said, turning to the Rabbis. "It's impossible. Ve both need somevone to take care of us. Ve're too sick to take care of each odder."

BEFORE BEGINNING their deliberations, the Rabbis asked Briendel for her opinion of the impending divorce. With a great *krechtz*, followed by two "*ais*" and accompanied by a giant "*oy*" from Zish as he finally sat down, she made her way to stand (or more accurately, lean) before the court.

"Whatever my husband says is fine with me," she said. "I want what's best for him." Slowly, she creaked back to where he was sitting.

That dispensed with, the Rabbis adjourned to their chambers. In the meantime, Zish and Briendel exchanged phone numbers, addresses and medical prescriptions.

Ten minutes later, the court reconvened. With a low but highly audible groan, Zish pulled himself out of his chair. Briendel felt too weak to move. "Mr. and Mrs. Gutnick, based on the medical and emotional evidence you have provided, it is obvious to us that you both need qualified people to care for you."

"Vhere do I sign?" asked Zish, congratulating himself for having presented the most compelling argument since Moshe took on Pharaoh in Egypt.

The *Av Beis Din* continued, "By the power vested in us as duly constituted members of this *Beis Din*, we hereby **deny** your request for divorce. You are to remain married to each other for the rest of your years."

Zish looked at Briendel with tears in his eyes. Briendel smiled back shyly. The same shy smile from Sami's Snackiya, Zish noted. They helped each other up and limped out of the courthouse together.

And they lived happily (*oy!*) ever (*ai!*) after.

Heard from: Rabbi David Aaron

Two for the Price of One

IF YOU HAD TO PICK the most "special" (my candidate for the most overused and least effective word in the current lexicon) Israeli city of all time, a number of towns would come to mind. Jerusalem, of course, with its Holy stones, Holy soil and Holy air. Tel Aviv with its incredible energy. Safed with its mystical serenity.

All good choices. But there's another Israeli city that's worth mentioning: New York, New York, a.k.a. the Big *Tapuach*. The City Everyone Loves to Hate. Home of the garment district, the diamond district, the theater district. Wall Street, Madison Avenue, the Lower East Side, the upper West Side. SoHo. TriBeCa, Greenwich Village. And on and on and on.

In truth, New York is more than a city. It's a place where you can be bred, wed, dead and buried, all without ever crossing its borders. For many New Yorkers, a trip out of the city is like a trip out of this world.

By last count, New York had more than 8 million residents of every race, color, creed and nationality you can imagine, including some 300,000 Israeli expatriates.

That's right, 300,000 Israelis! "*Yordim*" as they're known in the "old country," from the word *yored*, which means "to go down." To leave the Holy Land permanently is viewed as a deep descent, even if it's for the sake of a financial ascent.

Although Israelis who forsake their country are frowned upon, that hasn't stopped the masses from leaving. Month after month, they arrive by the dozens. Armed with a little English and a lot of ambition, they hit Kennedy Airport and never look back. It's as if America were beckoning: "Give me your tired, your poor, your starving Israelis yearning to be rich!"

To be fair, many Israelis have emigrated in order to help family members back home. Some have actually returned once they've achieved their financial goals. But for hundreds of thousands, America is the last stop on the road away from Judaism.

OPHER GABBAI was one of the former. A fourth generation Jerusalemite, he had come to Brooklyn in the hope of earning enough to support his seven younger brothers and sisters who remained in the Homeland. The route he chose was the same as that of many of his fellow expatriates — driving a taxi, or "car service" as it's known in that borough.

Working as a cabbie may not have been the most lucrative job Opher could have landed, but it had its advantages. For one thing, he could work whenever he wanted. For another, he was his own boss. Third, he never had to stray too far from the Jewish neighborhoods of Brooklyn.

Day after day, Opher shlepped people and occasionally packages from one part of the city to another. Sometimes he was used as a courier by various Jewish merchants. In every case, he tried to treat his customers the way he himself would have liked to be treated.

Furthermore, there was a deeper reason why this kind-hearted cabbie liked his profession. It gave him endless opportunities to do *mitzvos*; for not only would Opher give you the shirt off his back, he would wash and iron it first.

His taxi was his wings; Providence was his co-pilot. When he felt he had earned enough for the day, he stayed behind the wheel driving *meshulachim* on the beat he knew best.

ONCE when he took a fund solicitor for an Israeli yeshivah to a new address, he found himself at Grossman's Trophies, a huge building that had its own parking lot filled with cars. A tinted glass showcase displayed dozens of awards, medallions and trophies of every size, shape and description. Opher wondered whether this was the twentieth-century version of Terach's idol shop.

"I'll be right back," the solicitor informed Opher. "This shouldn't take long."

He was right. Almost instantly, he came out with a shrug and a half-smile.

"How did it go?" Opher asked.

"I got two dollars."

"That's all?"

"The owner said he couldn't afford more."

Opher was stunned. "Do you mind if I try?"

"Why not?"

Five minutes later, Opher returned. With a broad grin, he handed over fifty dollars in cash to his passenger.

The fund solicitor's eyebrows shot up in amazement.

"I came up with a payment plan," Opher hastened to explain.

"What do you mean?"

"I simply told him that if he didn't give you a proper donation, I would bring every *meshulach* I could find here! I think he preferred the cash-in-advance scheme!"

ONE DAY, Opher got a dispatch to the Sanzer *Beis Din* in Boro Park. From a block away he could see his passenger waiting at the steps, a young woman, maybe twenty years old, with the olive complexion and dark coloring that revealed her Middle Eastern origins. Opher greeted her in Hebrew, but the woman could not understand.

"Excuse me, I don't speak Hebrew. Only English or Farsi," she said.

"I'm sorry," Opher said. "Where are you going?"

"I don't know," she replied. "I just don't know." And then she began to weep.

Gotham City is a tough training ground for the emotions, and after so many years in New York, Opher thought he was inured to most sights and sounds. He was wrong; a sobbing twenty-year-old touched his heart.

"Is something the matter? Can I be of help?"

Shlomit Bar Kahana removed a tissue from her purse and dabbed at her eyes. Little streaks of make-up began to blur around her eyelashes as, between sobs, she commenced her story:

"Close to two years ago, my family arranged for me to leave Iran. My father had to pay a fortune, and my mother had to bear the separation most women will never know. I came, through Vienna, to the Shem Tov family here in Brooklyn. While I was living with them, I met another Iranian, and you know how these things go, both of us were lonely without family to look into matters for us, and in no time we were married. Not much..."

In mid-sentence Shlomit dissolved in a fit of soul-wrenching crying. It took some minutes of Opher's tender sympathy and encouragement before she could gulp back her tears and continue. "Now my husband has thrown me out, and refuses to give me a *get* unless I pay him $15,000. This *Beis Din*, like all of the others, cannot help me."

Opher understood just what she meant. The power of *Beis Din* emanates from the social pressure it commands and can marshal. Her husband was too much of an outsider to be affected by any pressure it could bring to bear. "Don't you have *anyone* who can help you?"

"No. The Shem Tovs have moved to Israel and they were the source of all my connections. I cannot contact my family in Iran, but even if there were a way, I could not allow myself to subject them to such disgrace. So right now, I have no home. No money. No job. And now, no hope." Big tears welled up in the corners of her eyes.

Opher couldn't endure such sadness. He tried to comfort her. "Please stop. The Talmud teaches that God's throne of glory cries when a marriage is terminated, and if His throne is crying... that's enough sadness."

"But what am I going to do?"

"We'll think of something," said Opher. "I'm sure I can help."

"How?"

"I can try talking to your husband."

"It's impossible. He wouldn't listen to the *day-yanim*; why would he listen to you?"

"Maybe because I'm not a judge."

OPHER took down her particulars and her husband's full name and address. After dropping Shlomit off at her girlfriend's apartment he drove out to Queens, hoping to catch Mr. Bar Kahana at home.

As he pulled up, he saw a slight, angular young man coming down the steps out of a modest Flushing home.

"Mr. Bar Kahana?" Opher called, still in his car.

"I did not call a cab," Bar Kahana said.

"I know. May I have a word with you?"

"Who are you? What do you want?"

Opher climbed out of his taxi and stepped up to Bar Kahana. "I took your wife home from the Sanzer *Beis Din* today," he said. "She told me that you are demanding $15,000 to deliver a *get*."

"And since when do cab drivers get involved with their passengers?" Bar Kahana demanded.

"Whenever it's a mitzvah. How do you expect her to come up with that amount of money?"

"Her family never asked *mine* that question. Prior to the wedding my brothers and sisters had to beg and borrow $15,000 before her family would agree to the marriage."

"Therefore?" Opher challenged. "Shlomit has no one here to help her. You might as well be realistic."

"Realistic? If she wanted, she could buy you and your cab several times over. My parents know her parents back in Iran. They're rich. Very rich. I'm sure she has money somewhere. She didn't spend it when we were together. So let her spend it now!"

Opher stared at Bar Kahana. "You're making a mistake. The girl has no money."

Bar Kahana shot back, "Fifteen thousand dollars is not a lot of money. If she wants a *get*, that's what it's going to take. Now, get out of my way!" With a cold look of disdain, Bar Kahana got into his car and drove off, leaving Opher Gabbai at the curbside, shaking his head.

"What a charming fellow," he quipped sarcastically to himself. "Well, at least I tried."

The next day, he went back to the apartment where Shlomit was staying to explain what had happened. Shlomit wasn't surprised.

"That's just like him," she said sadly. "I told him over and over again that even though my parents were able to get me out, their money remains in Iran. Believe me, they need every penny to stay alive."

"Are you sure you can't contact them and get their help?" Opher asked.

"What should I tell them? That my marriage didn't work? That I'm being held prisoner by my former husband? That I miss them so much I want to go back? Would that make them feel better?"

Opher just listened as the distraught girl went on. "You must understand, I cannot let them know what is going on here. They sacrificed so much. To tell them that my escape has turned into a nightmare would destroy them."

Shlomit began to tremble. Opher looked away and said quietly, "I'll see what I can do."

"No, no. You've done enough. Thank you, anyway." She walked Opher to the door. As he made his way down the hall, Shlomit's anguished cries followed him.

"Fifteen thousand dollars. It *is* a lot of money, but not an impossible sum to raise," he told himself. "Maybe I can get it from some of my mitzvah people. Then again, he pondered, "Maybe I should discuss this with a Rabbi first."

Opher drove over to the study of a renowned halachic authority and related the story. The Rabbi was adamant that in general one may not surrender to extortion of this nature. Opher pressed that this case was truly an exception since Shlomit was all alone and conventional means would be ineffective to coerce her husband to give a *get*. The Rabbi conceded the point and presented Opher with his first donation.

OVER THE NEXT FEW DAYS, Opher went to see several of his friends. From one, he picked up a pledge of $1,500. From another, $500 more. From a third, an additional $1,000. By the end of the week, he had raised half the money. But where he was going to find the other half he just didn't know.

Shabbos came and, as usual, he spent it at the

Rabinowitz *shul* in Flatbush. The Rabinowitz *shul* is a *shtiebel* with a capital "S." There, men, women and children *daven*ed, learned, shmoozed, *kid-dish*ed, ate, played and argued, living every minute of Shabbos to the utmost.

During the course of the day, Opher mentioned the situation of the *agunah* to the *shul*'s spiritual leader, Rabbi Steinfeld.

"How could it be that *Hashem* ransoms a person for money?" Opher asked urgently as he finished his story.

"Perhaps God has other plans for these people that we don't comprehend. Things may just work out in a way that you don't expect."

"Oh, I'm sure God knows what He's doing. But what should *I* be doing? That's what I want to know."

"You keep trying. That's your job. The Almighty will do what He sees fit. But you just keep trying."

"All right, but I've run out of mitzvah people," Opher said with a worried sigh. "And I still have $7,500 to go. Do you know anyone with that kind of money?"

"No, not really. Wait, I do have a name you could try. Hanna Margolis. She's a lawyer in Queens. Tell her I suggested you contact her. If she can't give you a big check, maybe she knows someone who can."

OPHER mentally filed the name Hanna Margolis for after Shabbos. He originally intended to contact her on Monday, but found himself with more work than he had expected. A jewelry convention was in town, and retailers and wholesalers from around the world were flocking to New York. Since many of them used the convention as an excuse to see relatives in Brooklyn, Opher spent the next few days shuttling merchants from borough to borough.

Finally, he got a fare that took him to Queens, and the name Hanna Margolis magically popped back into his head.

Opher looked up her address and zeroed in. He pulled up in front of a two-family brick house with well-beveled steps. On the front lawn, a fancy sign was staked into the ground: Hanna R. Margolis, Attorney-at-Law.

Opher Gabbai usually wasn't shy. But the idea of approaching a total stranger, especially a female stranger, for *tzedakah* didn't appeal to him.

Still, his Rabbi had told him to go, so Opher took a deep breath, and pushed himself out of the car and up the steps to the house.

He was about to ring the bell when he noticed that the door was slightly ajar. He spread out the few remaining hairs on his balding pate, brushed down his shirt front and stepped inside the parlor area where a receptionist was busily typing papers.

"Do you have an appointment?" she asked without glancing up.

"No, I've come to speak with Ms. Margolis about an urgent matter. Rabbi Steinfeld sent me."

"One minute, please. I'll see if she's available."

As Opher pantomimed and rehearsed his appeal, he was interrupted by a "May I help you?"

Opher looked up to see a slim woman in early middle-age, peering out with keen eyes from behind a pair of thick eyeglasses.

"Yes, thank you. Rabbi Steinfeld suggested that I contact you about a young woman in Boro Park who needs help."

"Come into my office," Hanna Margolis said with brisk efficiency.

Opher followed her past the reception area and into the dining room that served as her office.

"Sit down, please." Her voice had a tone of quiet authority as she took her seat behind a massive mahogany desk.

OPHER FELT AWKWARD and uncomfortable but did as he was told. For the next few minutes, he explained the entire sorry situation: Her background. His demand. Her refusal. His response.

When Opher finished, he waited for some response but noticed only a slightly faraway look in the eyes behind the glasses. Opher came to the point of the meeting. "So far, I've raised $7,500 out of the $15,000. Rabbi Steinfeld said you might be able to help with the rest."

"He did?" The keen eyes narrowed.

"Yes, he said you might either be able to donate a good amount or know someone who could."

Hanna Margolis' gaze dropped to the floor, then rose slowly to meet Opher's. "I'm sorry," she said quietly. "Please tell Rabbi Steinfeld I am a lawyer, not a banker or an accountant. I'm afraid I can't help you. My secretary will show you out."

"I'm sure he knows your profession, but something, *anything*, would be appreciated... If you only knew what this woman is going through!"

"I will think about it. That's all I can say. If you wish, you may leave your number with my secretary. Good day!"

Opher got up to leave. "Thank you for your time," he said. But the counselor was already too involved in some documents to hear.

Opher was in a foul mood as he left Queens for Brooklyn. "What a waste of time!" he railed. "I'll just have to try something else."

WHILE OPHER was struggling to come up with some new ideas, Hanna Margolis was involved in a struggle of her own. "Why should I give money to someone from Boro Park whom I don't even know?" she asked herself later that night. "When I needed help, no one gave anything to me."

Hanna Margolis looked back over her own life. Her father had died when she was just a toddler. Her mother remarried, but it just wasn't the same. Hanna ended up putting herself through Stern College and then Columbia Law School.

After law school, Hanna moved to Monsey and

began working for a firm in Manhattan. After a while she found the commuting exhausting, and had a need to change locales. The time had come to open her own practice, which she did with her move to Queens. For the last six years, Hanna Margolis had been building a reputation and a very successful career.

Now she reviewed her conversation with the cab driver. One sentence he had said stuck obstinately in her mind, "If you only knew what she was going through."

For his part, Opher began trying every long shot he could think of. He went to free-loan agencies, he went to wealthy and not-so-wealthy individuals, he even went to Hebrew school teachers. Eventually he even went back to Mr. Grossman of Grossman's Trophies. Everywhere the result was the same: It wasn't as if he had bad luck; he had no luck at all.

O NE DAY, he got a call for a pick-up in Queens. The address was vaguely familiar, but he couldn't place it right away. As he crawled his way out the Brooklyn-Queens Expressway, it hit him.

"That's Hanna Margolis' address!"

Out of excitement and curiosity, he gunned the motor and proceeded on the service road, hoping to make the time fly faster that way. Still it took him forty-five minutes to get there. He pulled up in front of her office, charged up the steps, and flung open the door. There was a new receptionist behind the desk.

"My name is Gabbai. I'm here to see Ms. Margolis."

"I'm afraid she's unavailable at the moment, but she did leave this envelope for you."

Opher scooped up the envelope, did an about-face and went out. The envelope was addressed to Shlomit Bar Kahana, but it wasn't sealed. Inside was a check for $7,500.

"*Baruch Hashem!*" he exclaimed.

As fast as he had outwitted the traffic to Queens, he drove even faster back to Boro Park. At Shlomit's apartment, he was brief and to the point.

"Our Sages have said that the *Geulah* can come at any moment. For you, it just has."

Shlomit looked at the check, then back at him. Once again her dark eyes began to well with tears. Only this time, they were tears of joy.

OPHER GABBAI always remembered the episode with Hanna Margolis and Shlomit Bar Kahana with a mixture of sadness, fascination, and gratitude. Sadness that an *agunah*'s plight could be so desperate. Fascination at the widely different personalities of the individuals involved. And gratitude to the Lord that everything had worked out in the end.

Still, Opher couldn't afford to dwell too much on the past. There remained a lot in the present that required his attention, especially when it came to collecting *tzedakah*. It was about three months after the Bar Kahana affair was over when Opher received a check for $500 from Hanna Margolis. There was no explanation, just a note that read, "Please give this to *tzedakah*." Opher had no trouble locating a needy family.

He kept hoping there would be no more people to collect for, but that was never the case. During the next six months, he managed to raise money for a yeshivah whose mortgage payments were in arrears, buy a brand new pair of *tefillin* for a Russian immigrant, and contribute to various and sundry worthy charitable causes.

Most recently, Opher took up a collection for an Israeli family who had come to America in order to have life-saving surgery for their child. The patient was doing fine, thank God, but the bills which were streaming in were a disease in themselves. The family had no one to turn to but the Jewish community.

Opher went over his "hit list." Basch, Berman, Friedman, Goldberg... For one reason or another, most of them were committed to other projects. Finally, he came to Hanna Margolis.

"Well, I haven't contacted her in a few months. I might as well try."

THAT NIGHT, when he finished his shift, Opher drove his cab to the lawyer's home. He was surprised to see that the sign outside had been changed. It now read Hanna Goldberg, Attorney-at-Law.

"Ah ha, a *mazal tov!*" Opher rejoiced.

Two rings of the doorbell later, he was in the parlor that still served as Hanna's reception area. "Mr. Gabbai! What can I do for you?"

"There's a little boy in Pittsburgh…"

"Pittsburgh? You're driving people to Pittsburgh?" she asked with a knowing smile.

"No, no. This is a friend of a friend. Her son had surgery out there. Thank God, he's doing fine. Now the family needs a cure for their bills."

"I'll be happy to give something. I assume you got my last check?"

"Oh, yes!" Opher replied. "*Todah rabbah.* It was used to help a young couple get married. By the way, *mazal tov.* I saw your new sign outside. When did this happen?"

Hanna laughed, a sad, bitter laugh. "About fifteen years ago."

"What?!"

"Yes. You see, I was married fifteen years ago. Margolis was my married name. After five years of marriage, my husband left me. I sent you that $500 check when I finally got my divorce."

"You mean when I first met you…"

"That's right… I, too, was an *agunah.* Obviously helping you to help Shlomit was what it took to earn my own release. Right after I gave you the check, out of the blue, my husband showed up, and finally agreed to a divorce."

Heard from: Les Rechoute

FOUR

Emergency

DEPARTMENT IV-B-4." Sounds like an address on an interoffice memo. However, to those familiar with European Jewish history, there was no designation more dreaded. The officers comprising this elite death squad were freaks of nature: they were more ruthless and cruel than is humanly possible.

On March 12, 1944, all of the SS officers of Eichmann's Department IV-B-4 were assembled in Mauthausen for the final planning of Operation Margarethe, the German occupation of Hungary. It was to be an operation conducted in record time, sweeping west from province to province, and leaving Budapest for last.

Months after Eichmann and his cohorts had finalized their plans, Sender Friedberg, in the heart of Margarethe territory, was contemplating his. An innately cheerful individual blessed with a prodigious wit, Sender was also well aware — far more aware than most of his contemporaries — of the clouds of doom gathering on the horizon, and he was busy planning his contingencies.

THERE WASN'T MUCH in his arsenal. He, his wife and two daughters were shunted into a tiny apartment in the ghetto together with 22 strangers. There was barely room to think, let alone devise a plan to escape with his life. The starving conditions, rampant disease, and sub-freezing weather also did little to enhance the prospects.

That left Sender with his wit alone to resolve his dilemma. His sharp mind had served him well in the past, but never were the circumstances of any comparable dimension.

How he would get his family out of Hungary was a problem that he would have to deal with; but before that was the more immediate problem of getting out of the ghetto. Staying in the ghetto constituted a choice between dying of starvation and being deported, which might be a slower or quicker route to the same end, depending. The

Nazi mind liked to keep its victims' options to a minimum.

ESCAPE from the ghetto was by no means a facile endeavor, and even if carefully executed, avoiding detection on the outside was equally formidable. Sender's first step was to remove the yellow star sewn onto his coat. Of course, without papers identifying him as a non-Jew this action was entirely pointless, but not nearly as pointless as inaction.

Even with guards, sentries and Gestapo officers virtually everywhere, conducting searches and spot checks on any possible culprit guilty of the crime of Judaism, Friedberg felt that he had to take the risk. And for Sender the risk was compounded by a factor over which he had no control: no one could have looked more stereotypically Jewish than he.

It was small wonder, then, that not long after he had escaped from the ghetto, while he was riding on a streetcar — a major crime in Nazi-occupied Hungary — his cover was blown. Two Gentiles, former neighbors and associates, recognized him. Solid citizens with a profound dedication to upholding the law, they considered it their civic duty to mete out Sender's death sentence immediately. Besides, it wasn't fair that the Nazis had all the fun.

With a gleam in their eyes and a sense of mission in their gait, they cornered the defenseless Jew. They delivered a few swift kicks as a pre-farewell, then lifted his emaciated body and heaved him off the rapidly moving trolley. Sender didn't exit without a struggle, but he was no match for a carload of well-fed citizens determined to make their country *Judenrein*. With a send-off not designed for him to remember, Sender was jettisoned directly into the street, right in the path of oncoming traffic.

Sender's right shoulder, which sustained the full impact of his fall, was flattened and his head rammed into a steel grating with a sickening thud. His skull was lacerated, two ribs were cracked, and his left arm was fractured in several places; but his body had fortuitously tumbled into a narrow, little traveled alleyway.

DROWNING in a puddle of his innocent blood, Sender, for all his wit, had no solution to his predicament. His body was all but glued to the steel, and he had no strength to unglue himself. If ever prayer alone could help, this was the time when it was needed. Sender strained his throbbing head to offer up what he was sure would be his last supplication, when salvation suddenly arrived.

A local merchant dumping his trash came across the grisly sight. Inexplicably, it thrust him into a moral dilemma that apparently failed to trouble his fellow countrymen. There could be no doubt that the mangled body bleeding all over the cobblestones belonged to a Jew. But then again, the Magyar peasants did have a tendency to get drunk and do all kinds of weird things.

Possible? Maybe. Probable? Surely not. But an

excuse? Conceivable. But then again, to leave him there would certainly be the easiest, and safest, thing to do. To bring him home, while certainly the most humane and moral thing to do, would also be the most reckless.

Contemplating his options, the merchant suddenly spotted the familiar insignia of a taxi barreling down the street and a new idea popped into his head. He flagged down the cab and unceremoniously loaded his cargo and himself aboard. Then he instructed the driver to proceed to the hospital and to leave the motor running while he hauled the body inside. This way he could make a risk-free drop-off and relieve his conscience at the same time.

THE HOSPITAL STAFF, individuals who had taken the Hippocratic oath, discovered the delivery on their doorstep, and were enjoined by their vow to treat and to heal. Sender's wounds were dressed and his fractured bones splinted. No embarrassing questions were asked, but since they suspected what the answers might be, they decided that they would release their undesirable patient from the hospital as quickly as possible.

There was no time for recovery, or for the pain to diminish. As soon as he could crawl out the front door he would be on his way to a second rendezvous with the fate that he had escaped the first time around.

Sender's head, although ravaged and beleaguered, was hard at work. The Prophet declared,

"If I have fallen, I will yet rise," and Sender concluded that since he had fulfilled the first part of the verse so literally, he was honor-bound to fulfill the second.

LATE AT NIGHT Sender perfected his plan and then, driven by his survival instinct, he mustered the strength and the stamina to carry it through. Feigning sleep, he waited for the ward to be deserted of hospital personnel before sliding down from his bed. Half limping, half shuffling, Sender stealthily made his way over to the ward's clothing closet where he found and immediately expropriated an oversized military coat, trousers and identification papers to match. This expropriation was executed under the nose of the very soldier whose very job it was (when awake) to guard the very closet that Friedberg had verily violated.

And then, only hours before he would have been released, the newly incarnated SS-Sturmbannführer Istvan Rakoczi made his way outside.

Propelled by a desire to be reunited with his family, and a taste of freedom on the tip of his tongue, Sender carefully headed back to the ghetto. But now there was no need for stealth. No one impeded his progress and, in fact, some saluted him with that repugnant, stiff-armed "Heil Hitler!" All in all, getting back into the ghetto was a lot easier than getting out had been. Soon, to the sheer astonishment, gratitude and utter joy of his family, the medical miracle squeezed into his former quarters.

Sender's face was swollen, he was badly injured and barely recognizable, especially in that strange uniform, but he was *alive*! The pitiful circumstances were such that there was no way to nurse him back to health in the ghetto. There were no medications or food, not even a bed. With 26 people crowded into one small room, there was barely enough space to lie sideways on the floor.

S EEING THE UNSINKABLE Sender Friedberg again, despite his pathetic condition, gave Ruth, his wife, a new lease on life. She was ecstatic to have him back. Little did she know that her pleasure was to be ephemeral, for Sender had not returned in order to be tended to, but to provide for his family. Although his body was weak and in pain, he was mentally as agile as ever and that would have to compensate for his physical disability.

Ruth greeted Sender's expressed intention to embark on a food-gathering foray with incredulity. "You must have injured your head even worse than it appears," she commented. "You see what happened to you the last time you left the ghetto. The next time..." and she paused as the irony of her next words struck her, "you may not be so lucky."

Had Sender's physiognomy not been so swollen and disfigured, Ruth might have noticed the twinkle in her husband's eye. With a battered body racked with pain serving as a constant warning not to repeat earlier errors, Sender carefully planned his new scheme.

VERY EARLY the next morning, under cover of darkness and in violation of the curfew, Sender scaled the ghetto wall. His flight to freedom was marked by an uneventful flop into a narrow passage. Momentarily stunned by the impact, Sender picked himself up with care, deliberateness *and* dignity. The man now rising from the ground adjacent to the prison which housed Budapest's Jewry was no longer Sender Friedberg, a learned furrier; it was none other than Sturmbannführer Istvan Rakoczi, the famous (although as yet little publicized) Hungarian Nazi war hero who had singlehandedly killed scores of Russian infantrymen and spearheaded his troops' advance in countless battles. If there was ever a loyal Hungarian Nazi, it was he. Although he had been badly wounded saving his country from the Allies, he still, as befit a national hero, maintained his dignity and savoir-faire.

Despite the harried circumstances, Sender had stolen his identification papers with care. The hospital he had escaped from had numerous wounded Hungarian officers that the Nazis deemed worthy of top-rate medical care. The talk of the ward, however, had been a decorated officer whose various wounds had diminished his pompous verbosity not one iota.

Considering the severity of the Nazi's wounds, Sender figured it would be some time before there were two Sturmbannführer Rakoczis limping around, bragging of their accomplishments.

SENDER KNEW he'd have no trouble with his new ID standing up to casual scrutiny, even

though he looked nothing like his "namesake."
With his head an orb of bandages and his torso
and limbs a mass of dressings, splints and slings,
he looked nothing like anyone. The real problem
was to be able to stand up to *intensive* scrutiny...
or avoid scrutiny altogether.

To this end, Sender headed for Nazi headquarters. In the dim, predawn light, he limped through
the front door as if he owned the place and strode
up to the young night duty officer. At this hour,
headquarters was almost deserted, or so Sender
had hoped.

The young soldier swiftly rose to salute a superior officer and Sender nearly turned around to
see who it was before he realized it was he. Casually, he returned the salute. "I assume you know
who I am," he said in a voice that mimicked the
pompous owner of his purloined uniform. "I am
SS-Sturmbannführer Rakoczi. These are my
papers. I require a pass that will enable me to
travel unmolested."

"But... but..." the duty officer protested.

Sender silenced him with a wave of his
mangled hand. "Were I able to write," he threatened, the bandages over his mouth muffling his
imperfect German accent, "I would record your
name and number and report you this very day
for insubordination!"

The youthful clerk paled visibly. "Just one
m-moment p-please, sir," he stammered.

Before long Sender was limping back out onto

the street with the precious pass in his pocket. He was now decidedly safer than any other Jew in Budapest but, for the time being, no better fed.

WITH THE FIRST STAGE of his plan completed, Sender was ready for Stage 2. His new get-up and persona enabled him to enter and exit the ghetto at leisure — through the main gate, no less. Once inside, and well out of sight of the guards who had admitted him, he interviewed fellow inmates regarding their contacts in the outside world. Whoever had close Gentile friends or contraband that could be used to buy favors gave Sender the information. Then, under the guise of carrying out some military duty, he visited the addresses he was given to procure food and provisions clandestinely. For his part in the operation, he got to keep a percentage of the food as his commission, a quantity sufficient to sustain his family and others who suffered horribly.

This became his daily routine, and as a result of his frequent forays to the outside, Sender became knowledgeable about the latest developments. One day, as he made his regular well-timed visit to the ghetto, he learned that the Germans were planning to blow up most of the compound *that very night.*

That didn't leave much time for Sender to get his family out of the ghetto. Digging a tunnel was as unlikely as an air evacuation. Once again Sender put his crisis-honed mind to the task. The result was an elaborate scheme which entailed as much ingenuity as plain, unadulterated guts.

DIRECTLY OUTSIDE the ghetto was an emergency medical station. In normal times and under normal circumstances each and every prisoner locked up in the ghetto could have qualified as a medical emergency, but in Nazi times and under Nazi circumstances, none of them qualified. Zombie-like subsistence at the brink of death was hardly an emergency if the zombie were a Jew; indeed, to the Nazi mind, it was desirable, second only to death itself.

A risk to a German life, however, was indeed an emergency. Accordingly, Sender searched for just the right threat. His feverish investigations revealed that ingesting ground up chalk did wonders for lowering blood pressure and could make the consumer seem to be even more ill than he already was.

In less than an hour he had located the ingredient and prepared the recipe. But it was now afternoon and the escape had still not been secured. There was no time to spare. Sender administered the instant disease to his family and hurried off to the emergency station to case the joint and establish any contacts possible. Twenty-five minutes before sunset, his plan was complete.

FOR THE RIGHT BRIBE Sender was able to "borrow" a car and evacuate his ailing wife and daughters (plagued with a rare and highly contagious disease) from the ghetto. An outbreak of this malady could have threatened the health and well-being of the Nazis deployed there. Once

Sender had his family admitted to the emergency station, he left his wife in the care of a doctor as pre-arranged. Then, before anyone was the wiser, he smuggled his two daughters back to the car via a circuitous route that avoided the Nazi guards charged with preventing such two-way traffic at the medical station.

Sender surgically redesigned his daughters' clothing to remove any trace of the yellow stars they had borne. The girls were then delivered to a Catholic convent. None but the Abbot was aware of their background and he was assured by a loyal Hungarian Nazi officer that the girls' parents had already been deported and would never return. Under those conditions, the cleric was willing to accept the would-be converts.

Stage 3 of Sender's elaborate plan was complete, and everyone was out of immediate danger. The time had come to devote all of his energies to Stage 4: escape from Budapest. As Sender contemplated his next move, dramatic events were unfolding all around.

HITLER was enraged that the Final Solution for Hungary's 800,000 Jews had not yet been completed. He sent his most zealous henchman, Adolph Eichmann, to solve the Jewish Problem in Hungary. With the newly installed puppet German government under General Szto-pay and the Arrow Cross (Hungarian Nazis) help-ing Eichmann, the newly created War Refugee Board in America realized that the last large re-maining Jewish population in Europe was facing extermination.

The Allies rejected the idea of bombing the rail-road lines leading to Auschwitz because, they said, military resources could be better used else-where. By July of 1944, some 400,000 Hungarian Jews had been deported to Auschwitz for extermi-nation; 200,000 more remained in various depor-tation centers and concentration camps. In Budapest, 200,000 others were being held pris-oner inside ghetto walls.

Secretary of State Cordell Hull asked neutral nations of the world to send additional diplomats to Budapest to help save the Jews. Though nu-merous neutral governments instructed their embassies to help, only the Swedes responded and Raoul Wallenberg volunteered for the job. The Swedish government felt remorseful over the fact that in the early stages of the war, when country after country was falling before the Nazi onslaught, they had allowed the German armed forces transit rights across their territory to Nor-way and Finland. Now that it was clear that the Germans were going to lose the war, the Swedes were less fearful of offending them.

Wallenberg went to Hungary with the authori-zation of the War Refugee Board, American money, and Swedish diplomatic papers. Raoul was assigned as the First Secretary to the

Swedish legation in Budapest. Before leaving for Hungary, he negotiated with the Swedish Foreign Ministry to have a free hand to use whatever methods he needed in order to save as many lives as possible.

He originally planned to go to Hungary in August; however, after reading Swedish Foreign Ministry reports from Budapest, Raoul left immediately, knowing that every moment lost would cost human lives. He was aware of the urgency of the situation as well as the dangers awaiting him.

WALLENBERG arrived in Budapest from Berlin on July 9, 1944. The train which brought him to Budapest had passed a train of 29 sealed cattle cars transporting the last batch of Hungary's provincial Jews to Auschwitz. Eichmann was so proud of the speed of the operation that he dubbed it, "A deportation surpassing every preceding deportation in magnitude." At that point only 230,000 terrified Jews remained trapped in the capital.

Emboldened by his success in the provinces, Eichmann prepared an audacious plan to round up the entire Jewish population of Budapest in a stunning twenty-four-hour blitz. Auschwitz, however, was unable to cope with the increased volume. Even with the extra ovens, gas chambers, and rail lines recently installed in honor of Hungarian Jewry, the quantity was too great. Thus Eichmann reluctantly agreed to a reduced schedule of three transports a day.

A separate problem was the advancing Russian

army. Every piece of military hardware and certainly every train was vitally needed in the retreat. Accordingly, vital vehicles would be diverted from the extermination process. Eichmann appealed directly to Himmler on the matter, and Himmler raised the problem with Hitler himself.

The Führer ruled that the army could claim priority on transport vehicles only when it was advancing, but since it was now *retreating*, Eichmann got his trains. Thus, at the most desperate stage of the war, with German troops pulling back across the plains of eastern Hungary — by foot — and with the Reich itself threatened, the annihilation of the Jews was still awarded the highest priority.

In the midst of this, Wallenberg informed his associates, "I came to save a nation," and it was his courage, dedication and shrewdness that allowed him to accomplish as much as he did. In carrying out his rescue operation, Wallenberg displayed an amazing lack of concern for his own safety and seemed miraculously immune from harm by the Nazis and their local hooligan supporters. Immediately organizing the remaining leaders of the Jewish community into a staff that later grew to over 400, Wallenberg arranged for these people to be exempt from wearing the yellow star, giving them the freedom to travel throughout the city. They kept Wallenberg informed of everything that happened in Budapest and enabled him to keep tabs on the activities and plans of the Nazis and the Hungarian Fascists.

PRIOR TO WALLENBERG'S ARRIVAL in Hungary, the Swedes and other neutrals in Budapest (thanks to the intervention of Charles Lutz and Friederich Born) had distributed hundreds of protective passes to Jews who had ties with their countries. One of the first things that Wallenberg realized was the importance of appearances when dealing with German and Hungarian officialdom, and he therefore designed a most impressive-looking Swedish passport to replace the somewhat mundane certificates that had been issued previously.

Printed in yellow and blue and embellished with the triple crown of the Royal Swedish government, dotted with seals, stamps, signatures and countersignatures, the new passport design was a stroke of genius. It had no validity whatsoever in international law, but its very appearance commanded respect, informing the Nazi officials that its holder was not an abandoned outcast but was under the protection of the leading neutral power in Europe, and simultaneously providing a morale boost to its bearer.

At first, the Hungarian Foreign Ministry gave Wallenberg permission to issue only 1,500 of these passports. By skillful negotiation, he got the quota increased to 2,500 and then to 4,500. In fact, he eventually issued more than three times that number, blackmailing Hungarian officials and bribing to turn a blind eye. When things really got desperate in the final days, he issued a far more simplified version bearing only his signature, and often that was sufficient to guarantee the document's acceptance as valid.

Wallenberg and his staff worked day and night printing and distributing these documents. Risking his personal safety time after time, Wallenberg climbed atop deportation trains carrying Jews to their death to distribute Swedish passes to all who could reach him. He then insisted that these people were under the protection of his government and told the SS officers they would have to allow them to detrain. Whenever he heard of a deportation train leaving for Auschwitz, Wallenberg would run to the station and ask, "Who here has Swedish papers?" Sometimes people without passes would hold up driver's licenses and other documents in Hungarian that the Germans could not read. Wallenberg would bully the officers at the station into letting these people leave with him.

With the American money he had brought, Wallenberg purchased 31 buildings in which to house the people he saved. He set up these safe houses along the west bank of the Danube, each flying the Swedish flag and guaranteeing shelter and refuge to hundreds of Jews. When necessary, Wallenberg dressed "Aryan-looking" Jewish men in SS uniforms and sent them to stand guard at these safe houses.

Sender was desperate to acquire papers for his family, so he quickly made his way to one of Wallenberg's safe houses. At this point, time was a factor more deadly than famine and pestilence. He did manage to register for documents for his family and now had to play the dangerous waiting game of staying out of sight, avoiding the round-ups, the *aktions*, and the Hungarian police.

Somehow he would have to hold out until the papers arrived.

I N DECEMBER 27, 1944, Sender got the Wallenberg papers for his family from the Portuguese State House, but by that time they were useless. There was such a glut of documents that no matter how richly they were stamped or how decoratively embossed, they were meaningless. The *aktion* had commenced and by the end of the week, according to Operation Margarethe, Budapest would be *Judenrein.*

A cold, bleak drizzle shrouded Hungary's capital as Sender began to run. Dragging a wounded leg and a pain-racked body, and clutching his worthless documents, he was headed nowhere, for there was no longer any place to go. His cover as a nationalist Nazi had been blown and now he was even more sought-after than the average Jew on the loose.

The earth was burning beneath his feet. And just as he had been found out, he knew that the other members of his family would also be discovered when the Nazis made their final purge to annihilate what remained of Hungarian Jewry.

Where was he running? He didn't know, but he felt compelled to dash down the corridors of a prison which had no exit. The twists of cruel irony gnawed ferociously at Sender's gut as he considered that all of his earlier escapades would do nothing to spare him the gas of Auschwitz.

H E CONTINUED RUNNING. His mind was racing and his feet were blazing and had the siren not blasted directly in his ear he probably would have been run over by the ambulance hurtling down the street. The vehicle screeched to a halt one block ahead of him, and Sender snarled, "Ha! They think *they* have an emergency. Some Nazi sprains his thumb and an entire emergency team has to cart him off to a hospital!"

Bearing a stretcher, the ambulance team descended and awkwardly made their way up to the home of Hermann Krumey, one of Eichmann's chief lieutenants in Budapest. As Sender watched the spectacle, the lightbulb that had always illuminated his mind with survival instincts and brilliant schemes to help his people, but which had temporarily dimmed, suddenly shimmered with stunning incandescence.

In seconds Sender commandeered the ambulance and took off down the road. Burning rubber all the way, he activated the siren, turned on the flashing lights, and clothed himself in the spare ambulance corps apparel that he found on the front seat.

S CREECHING TO A HALT like an ambulance driver truly on his way to an emergency, Sender pulled up in front of the medical station at Wesseleny Street. And while the EMT look-alike tore into the building, Miklos and Andras sidled out of a building several blocks away, precariously balancing on their stretcher the prostrate form of Mrs. Hermann Krumey, the charming wife of Eichmann's chief assistant in the deportation of the Jews.

As soon as they reached the street, consternation overcame these two medics of limited intelligence. They looked at the street and then looked at each other and then they looked back at the street.

"I'm sure I parked it over here," Miklos said to Andras.

"Obviously you didn't," Andras countered. "Maybe we left it around the corner."

Mrs. Krumey, accustomed to being waited *on* but not to waiting, began screaming in her typically feminine manner about the punishment that awaited her stretcher-bearers if they failed to take her to the hospital immediately. Catalyzed by the warning and a chilling perception of the infirm's undoubted Prussian precision in carrying out her threats, Miklos and Andras were quick to react. They both fled in different directions, searching for the ambulance and simultaneously dropping a bound and strapped Gretl Krumey into a pile of garbage massed on the curb.

Enveloped in slops and rot and gushing in trash, Mrs. Krumey managed to clear her mouth sufficiently to let out a barrage of pleasantries that made Miklos and Andras fear for their lives. They rushed back to the garbage pile and scooped out Madame Commandant from the debris.

"Do you know who I am?" she shouted. "Do you know who I am?" she ranted with remarkable stamina for someone so ill. "DO YOU KNOW WHO I AM??!??" she shrieked.

Miklos looked at Andras and shrugged. Andras looked at Miklos and shrugged. Suddenly all four eyes began to twinkle. "Do you know who I am?" they both asked.

Disarmed, in a figurative sense, Madame Commandant answered, "No," to which the pragmatists of the ambulance corps responded, "Good!" and dropped her just where they had found her. Krumey's splashdown was decidedly more dramatic this time than her earlier descent. The boys in white were last seen heading off into the horizon at a good clip.

MEANWHILE, Sender raced into the medical station brandishing his savoir-faire as if he had just been renominated Hungarian-Nazi patriot of the decade. He asked the medical personnel congregated in the hall where Friedberg was, for he had instructions to remove her immediately before she contaminated anyone *else*. His words galvanized the head nurse into action. She leaped up from her desk and from afar pointed out the patient's location.

"Everyone move away," Sender instructed as he whisked Ruth down the corridor. Despite his rush he overheard a snatch of a telephone conversation between one of the Hungarian Nazis assigned to guard the station and someone who was obviously his superior. He didn't hear the entire discussion, but thanks to the guard's repetition of the phone message as he jotted it down, Sender did catch one seminal phrase:

"...a stolen ambulance in the area..."

Sender took a deep breath and approached the guard. "Sir, forgive me but I overheard what you were discussing. I actually saw that ambulance on my way over here. It was involved in a terrible accident on the outskirts of town, about twenty-five kilometers from here, and you should inform the police to rush to the scene. The whole thing looked very suspicious to me... I'd love to supply you with more details but I've got an emergency of my own on my hands." Sender pointed to his wife. The guard nodded and reported the information to his superior.

Ruth was speechless. She wanted to ask how he had managed this one, but it was so fantastic that she couldn't find the words.

Sender picked up on her curiosity and winked at her reassuringly. "Next stop, Antoinette convent," he whispered.

FIFTEEN MINUTES LATER Sender made another dramatic entrance, this time at the convent, with his siren wailing and lights flashing. "I've come to pick up the two sisters who, I'm told, arrived here several weeks ago," he informed the nun who greeted him.

"They cannot be removed," the nun replied. "Our Abbot has them under special observation."

"I don't mean to take them away from the convent, God forbid," Sender told her most reverentially. "I was sent because of the medical emergency. I gather you were not the one who called, as you obviously are not aware of the gravity of their situation."

"Emergency!?" the nun echoed, totally agog.

"Of the highest order," Sender affirmed.

"I'm so sorry to have delayed," she apologized, and ran to fetch the two girls. Sender followed on her heels, and when he found his daughters, he scooped them up and rushed them outside to the ambulance. He took care to arrange the two girls to appear as one patient, with the sheet covering all but the hair of one at the upper end of the stretcher and feet of the other protruding at the bottom.

Then, with the help of the Nazis who expedited its exit at every checkpost, and a goodly helping of Divine assistance, the ambulance wailed its way right out of Budapest.

Deep in the countryside that was already *Judenrein*, the Friedbergs managed to live out the end of the war, aided by the many contacts that Sender had established earlier as a food courier.

Through his courage and resourcefulness, Sender Friedberg and Company had successfully thwarted all the meticulous planning of Department IV-B-4. Operation Margarethe was one Nazi operation in which the Jewish patient refused to lay down and die.

Heard from: Dovid Blau

Totally Awesome!

WHY SHMUEL Bernstein was selected to solicit funds for his yeshivah is a story in its own right, albeit a short one. A somewhat naive but nevertheless dedicated student, Shmuel never quite excelled in his studies. All right, let's call a spade a spade: Shmuel Bernstein's parents should have taught him a vocation. But *nobody* tried harder than Shmuel did. Avis could take a page from his book.

Shmuel was not so naive as to be ignorant of

his lack of success in learning. Still, he longed to make a lasting contribution to the field of Torah education. The dean of his suburban Jerusalem yeshivah, sensitive to the needs of all the students, hit upon the idea of sending Shmuel abroad, where he might at least manage to collect some not-so-lasting contributions. But why quibble? One contribution might turn out to be as meaningful as the other. Such a mission, furthermore, would give Shmuel a sense of purpose and boost his self-esteem, and, with bountiful blessings of Providence, the yeshivah would not lose out on the deal.

ALAS, FOR ALL THE *Rosh Yeshivah*'s good intentions, Shmuel Bernstein was simply not the man for the job. Remarkably, Bernstein did not come to that conclusion himself until he was already airborne on his search-and-solicit mission to Toronto. Somewhere over the Atlantic, the awesomeness of his agency suddenly dawned on him and he was seized with a fit of schnorrophobia. Shmuel's youthful imagination conjured up a vision of dozens of creditors pounding down the doors of the yeshivah — many-tentacled creatures named *Arnona*, *Bezek* and *Pazgaz*, hurling *shtenders* and *sefarim* into trash dumpsters and herding *roshei yeshivah* and students away in humiliation and disgrace.

"If I fail to bring back enough money, the yeshivah may close!" he realized, now lathered in sweat. "If I fail to raise enough to cover my trip, it definitely *will* close!" Shmuel began hyperventilating. His face turned chalky and he shivered with chills. His legs flailed in a nervous jig as his hands vise-clamped around the armrests. With anxiety contorting his features, he created something of a spectacle aboard the crowded plane.

"What's de matta?" asked an elderly gentleman seated on Shmuel's right. "Fear of flyin?"

"Er... no, I mean yes, I mean... I don't know."

The kindhearted, although not too subtle, neighbor saw that he had a case on his hands and placed a solicitous arm around Shmuel's twitching shoulder. "Ya got nuttin ta be scared of. My business takes me ta America nine times a year an I ain't falled out yet. Ha, ha! We're all in dis tugedder and dere's safety in numbers, so dere's nuttin ta worry 'bout."

But Shmuel was worried. The problem wasn't flying; it was landing. He had no training in soliciting funds and he lacked the necessary confidence to seek donations. Insecurity overwhelmed him, and the fear of returning to Israel penniless made his blood run cold.

"What, what?" his neighbor pressed. "Ya gonna keep dis *shvitzin* up de whole way, or what?"

"I'm afraid of collecting money," Shmuel blurted out. "That is, I'm afraid of *not* collecting money. That is, I'm afraid of failing!"

"Ohhh," the neighbor said, a knowing look in his eye, "a *greener* headed for Toronto. I see dey're startin ya in de majors, huh?"

Shmuel nodded silently.

"No problem, pal. We'll get yer act tugedder; we're all old pros here." The man gestured to his cronies seated nearby. "Fresh meat," he proclaimed, hooking a thumb at Shmuel. In milliseconds, fellow fund-raisers of every stripe began pouring out of every compartment of the plane, and an impromptu symposium on the do's, don'ts, and how-to's of fund raising was convened forthwith.

EVERYONE started offering advice on how to make it past the front door, how to counter "I gave already," how to conceal who sent you, etc., etc. Shmuel began scribbling copious notes, his head spinning dizzyingly as he tried to catch each and every tossed pearl of wisdom which might save his yeshivah from bankruptcy. But there was so much advice, flying in so many directions, that a tape recorder would not have been able to capture it all. One schnorrer after another graciously offered documentary proof of his expertise, with generous tips on the profession. The volume of voices reached a crescendo, and Shmuel's jaw gaped in incredulity.

Shmuel's neighbor, the ad hoc conference chairman, recognized the poor boy's dilemma and held up his hands for quiet. When calm was finally achieved, he informed the thirty or so delegates that, instead of imparting the secrets of the trade, they were only creating confusion. "We're all in dis tugedder," he reiterated in a voice of wizened authority, or at least seniority, "an it's only right we should help out dis newcomer ta our distinguished profession. But dis, dis ain't helpin nobody. We gotta be whajacallit, systematic."

The senior schnorrer looked around until he was sure he had everyone's consent, and then, with the sonorous tone of someone swearing in a Supreme Court Justice, he addressed the novice. "Dere's five basic rules ta fund raisin; no more an no less. If ya stick ta dese simple rules, ya got it made. Ya'll be a whajacallit, asset to yer yeshivah, an ya'll make a liddle *gelt* for yerself on de side. Got it? Good. Write dis down:

Rule #1: Dress neatly

Rule #2: Be polite

Rule #3: Compliment the host or hostess

Rule #4: Be brief

Rule #5: Speak the language of your patrons

"The rest is whajacallit, commentary. Take it from me, if ya stick ta dese rules, ya'll be a mitzvah magnet; ya can't lose." All of the delegates reverently nodded their heads and the meeting was summarily adjourned.

Shmuel dutifully copied the five rules on a fresh scrap of paper and stuffed it into his shirt pocket. Several times during the flight he consulted the cardinal rules, and just having them on his person imbued him with a warm feeling of confidence.

A T THE TORONTO AIRPORT Shmuel's comrades-in-alms arranged a ride for him to the *kollel* and secured a moonlighting taxi driver to take him to the Queen City's basic stops and attractions for *meshulachim*. As home visits were conducted only in the evenings, Shmuel had a whole day to rest up from his trip and prepare for his big debut.

Our hero slept fitfully, contemplating his upcoming appearance at the home of a local host. By early afternoon he despaired of getting any real sleep, so he hauled himself out of bed to begin his preparations. Suddenly, his mind was a blank. He quickly consulted his precious list.

Rule #1: Dress neatly

This seemingly simple rule would require a good deal of thought and effort on Shmuel's part. Neatness, like finesse, was not his forte, and he was wont to concoct his own original solutions to standard problems of grooming and attire. The fashion statement made by the young man's wardrobe was usually a resounding "*Nebach!*"

HE STOOD in front of a mirror and looked critically at his reflection. Working his way down from the top, Shmuel noticed that his shirt was horribly wrinkled; in fact, all the shirts he'd brought were — a credit no doubt to his inimitable manner of packing. Not having changed out of his best shirt for the past day-and-a-half hadn't helped its condition, but he stuck with it (literally, I'm afraid) out of a sense of passive loyalty. The patrons he would visit would see only the front of the collar and the least creased fields between his tie and jacket. This comforting thought allowed Shmuel to consider the shirt an integral part of the shirt/tie/jacket segment of his ensemble. The ink stain from a leaky ballpoint could easily pass for an emblem on the pocket, he assured himself, and with that touch of class he could allow himself to disregard a few wrinkle ranges here and there and a frayed cuff or two.

His tie, however, had no such redeeming invisibility. It wasn't merely stained; it was encrusted. Shmuel's method of cleaning it by rubbing a bar of soap over the globs of filth and lakes of soil only worsened the situation. *Post facto* he devised a rather unique solution, reversing his tie so that the stain-free inside was outside. Needless to say, the seam and lining were now clearly visible; but one had to admit that the tie at least looked clean.

Moving right along, Shmuel came to his belt, or actually his father's belt, which he had long ago cut down to his size. The simulated leather was a bit chapped — all right, missing in a few spots, and the loop was gone altogether, but when he rotated the buckle to the side, you couldn't tell that he'd punched the notches with a can opener.

His pants were not too bad, relatively speaking. Amazingly, there were no split seams, the few minor pizza-and-coke stains by now blended in more or less with the weave, and his jacket almost completely covered the shiny seat. His shoes, however, were in such a scuffed and dust-laden state that even Shmuel couldn't help but notice.

The would-be fund-raiser attempted to rectify that condition in the most expeditious way: Standing first on his left foot, he polished the uppers of his dusty right shoe against the back of his left trouser leg. Then he switched feet. There's no denying the effectiveness of the method, enhanced by some grease deposits formerly embedded in the fabric. However, the backs of Shmuel's pants from the knees down (which he could not see) were now caked with all the grime that had previously sullied his shoes.

Looking his best — emphasis on the "his" — Shmuel was ready to embark on his mission to raise desperately needed funds for his yeshivah. Remembering that the other rules for successful solicitation, which he intended to fulfill with equal exactitude, applied to the actual encounter, he slipped his list into an unholey pocket for later reference, finger-combed his hair, and sat down to wait.

IN THE EARLY EVENING Shmuel was picked up by a driver who asked if he wanted to be taken along the "regular route" or did Shmuel have some particular addresses in mind. Since he had been equipped by his yeshivah with a few leads to wealthy Torontonians, Shmuel fished around in his excuse-for-an attaché case (i.e., plastic shopping bag with snap-close handles) until he found the crumpled document. He read the first entry to the driver.

"Huh?" the man behind the wheel asked. "I never heard of such a place; you sure it's in Ontario?"

"It's got to be," Shmuel replied. "My yeshivah gave it to me."

"Uh, uh," grunted the driver, who was beginning to realize what he was in for with this raw recruit. "Let me hear what else you got."

Shmuel went over his entire list of leads with the driver, but only one place sounded familiar: 624 Prince Edward Drive. Unfortunately, the by now exasperated driver got his royalty confused and inadvertently delivered his unsuspecting passenger to 624 Prince Charles Drive.

Now, while Prince Charles did indeed reign in the Jewish part of town, his kingdom centered on the most assimilated section of the neighborhood. But assimilated by no means meant poor. In fact, the driver was enormously impressed with the residence that stood at his mistaken address, the most imposing edifice he'd ever encountered in a half-dozen years of motoring *meshulachim.*

THE HOUSE was a stately three-story Victorian affair with an octagonal tower dominating the right front corner. A large porch, defined by a complicated gingerbread trim, started at the tower, extended along the front of the house, and swept around the left side. Above the double-doored front entrance and resting on the roof of the porch was a circular balcony, roofed with a cone that complemented the one on top of the tower. The mansion had obviously cost a fortune, although at present it was terribly unkempt and in a state of neglect.

Since the driver was unable to find parking in the driveway, which hosted three unusual vehicles — a beat-up Land Rover, a beat-up dune buggy, and a very beat-up Thunderbird — he parked down the street to wait patiently for Shmuel to complete his business. By the look of things, he figured it was okay to leave the motor running.

"I usually work on percentages," he told the tyro *meshulach*. Shmuel had no idea what the driver meant. "But seeing as this is your first time out," he continued, tactfully not mentioning the unlikelihood of there being a sum to take a percentage of, "I'll just take a flat fee. Good luck."

Shmuel got out of the car and checked the side mirror to see if his hat was on in the right direction. It looked all right, but he wasn't sure. For good measure he rotated it a half-turn, tucked his shirttails in, and rebuffed his shoes on his pants legs. Static electricity crackled as serge and sock united around calf level, but all in all Shmuel looked neater than he ever had before. Still, there was always room for improvement.

He scrutinized his reflection again, trying to think of an extra bit of dash that would render him debonair enough to attract sizeable donations to his cause. Shmuel's innovative mind soon hit upon just the right accessory for his outfit. In lieu of a handkerchief, he inserted a tissue in the breast pocket of his jacket and fluffed it out artfully. Of special note were the two paperclips which from time immemorial had served as surrogate cufflinks.

S HMUEL TOOK A DEEP BREATH and strode up the walk to his very first house, hoping his lucky first knock would herald the first opportunity to help out his yeshivah. A most unusual aroma wafting from the window was inhaled along with his deep breath. The closer he got, the more pungent the smell became. Well, it couldn't be a sacrifice, he assured himself. Shmuel was at a loss to identify the bittersweet fragrance, but he wasn't about to let a little thing like that derail his mission.

When he reached up to knock on the door, he noticed the name engraved on the brass plate below the knocker: PEARLOWITZ. With his knuckled fist poised in mid-knock, he referred to his donor sheet, where the name "Pearlman" appeared. "A typo," he figured. His knuckles continued their journey.

An aging hippie wearing a peasant dress with long billowing sleeves, granny glasses and earth shoes greeted him with a peace sign. She was wearing no less than thirteen necklaces, all constructed from decorative findings as diverse as telephone wire, Wrigley gum wrappers, and aluminum pop tops.

Her every movement tinkled, as she was adorned from head to toe with bells of various sizes, dimensions and resonances. Even her big hoop earrings had bells on them. Needless to say, she had several bangle bracelets that added to the cacophony. Every finger boasted at least one ring made from unidentifiable debris, except for the two rings that were salvaged cigar bands.

"Mrs. Pearlman... eh, er... owitz?" Shmuel asked. There was no answer. She looked him over, twice or thrice, registering but resisting comment on his attire, and then flashed the peace sign again. Shmuel understood this second communication to be an invitation to enter, so our hero gallantly stepped over the threshold.

IT WOULD BE WRONG to say that Shmuel was undaunted. In reality, Shmuel was daunted. Very daunted. He was caught so much by surprise that he quickly consulted his trusty instruction manual to see how to proceed. Staring right at him was

Rule #2: Be polite

which he immediately activated. He thrust out a peace sign with both hands, looking for all the world like a politician who has just won the primary, and solemnly intoned a polite "Thank you."

Bernstein didn't get very far before he was practically knocked off his feet by the unusual odor which permeated the whole house. He noticed the tiny pots that littered the floor, polluting the air with tiny puffs of smoke. Remarkably, these pots were about the most normal thing on the floor. But before he could take in the entire scene the hostess inquired, "How can I help you?"

Shmuel was again thrown off guard and quickly checked his list.

Rule #3: Compliment the hostess

Eager to oblige, Shmuel offered, "Nice-smelling house you have here."

"It's a special brand; it really blows your Karma."

"Thank you," Shmuel responded, remembering Rule #2 and at the same time reaching new heights in non sequiturology.

"Mrs. Pearl..."

"No one's called me that for years. That's, like, you know, so, like, *antique!* Call me Ginger, and have a seat. My planet is yours!"

Bernstein didn't know what to make of this invitation. He'd never been asked to share someone's planet before. He looked all over for a chair. He looked to the left; he looked to the right. He even looked up. But all he saw were oversized cushions strewn across the floor. The decor of the house did not seem to be highly prioritized.

A carillon symphony alerted Shmuel to the fact that Ginger was about to be seated herself, and sure enough, as he watched, his hostess folded her legs underneath her and sat down lotus-like on a woven Indian rug. "*Oy!*" Shmuel thought to himself. "I could never do that in a million years!"

He was still standing when Ginger waved him toward one of the giant floor pillows that were scattered about the room like fabric boulders. "Man, there's no need to, like, stand on ceremony," she said. "Pull up a pillow and plop!"

Shmuel nodded dumbly and tried to sit on one of the cushions. It was a mistake. He instantly sank up to his eyeballs in kapok. "*Gevald!*" he cried out as he struggled to find a secure, if not comfortable, position.

"Don't fight it, man!" Ginger advised. "Just go with the flow! Relax!"

SHMUEL DIDN'T HAVE much choice. It was either stand tall or sprawl, and he desperately wanted to follow Rule #2: Be polite. So there he sat, or more accurately, lounged, in an overstuffed pillow, trying to make himself look as presentable and professional as he could under the circumstances.

"Now," Ginger said, "let's rap."

"Pardon me?"

"Let's RAP! You know, like, tell me what's on your mind and I'll, like, *respond!*"

Shmuel glanced again at his *meshulach*'s manual and again it did not fail him.

Rule #4: Be brief

Interpreting the instruction as literally as possible, he replied, "Charity."

Ginger pondered that for a moment. "I've got a fish named 'Faith' and a cat named 'Hope,' but there's no one here named 'Charity.'" Then she brightened. "You must mean 'Chastity,' my daughter!" With that, the mistress of the house reached behind her back, deftly raised a ceremonial stick that looked like a Louisville Slugger, and whacked a massive Oriental gong that stood in a corner. The sound sent shivers up Bernstein's spine, but they quickly passed. Little did he know he'd soon be needing them again.

A beaded curtain clattered and from behind it a voice yelled, "Yeah, Ginger? Whaddayawant?"

"You have, like, company, dear!"

"I'll be right there."

Ginger turned to her guest. "My daughter's, like, a heavy metal freak, you know?"

"I do?" Shmuel asked incredulously.

"Yeah. She can spend hours listening to punk rock, sometimes without even turning on her CD player. It drives me bananas. I mean, like, how can you live like that? All that violence. Things are meant to just *be*. Oh, I agree with her that order is really disorder and chaos is cosmic. But still, heavy metal is just *too* heavy for me. I think mellow is where it's at. You know, I mean, like, no one tells leaves on the trees where to fall; they just do their thing. We should do the same, don't you think?"

Shmuel was stumped. Out of desperation, he simply said, "R-r-r-right."

"Right *on!*" Ginger agreed, raising her clenched fist toward the sky. "Right *on*, brother!"

BEFORE SHMUEL could figure out what in heaven's name Ginger was saying, the beaded curtain parted. Shmuel thought it was a girl. But then he wasn't sure. It could have been a boy. She, or he, was dressed in black from head to toe. A long black shirt covered black jeans. A black leather jacket covered the long black shirt. Big black motorcycle boots topped off the costume at the bottom.

The effect was enhanced by the person inside the outfit. Her skin was so pale, she could have done a minstrel show, like Al Jolson singing "Mammy." Except for the hair. The sides of her head were totally shaven. The hair on top stood straight up like chicken feathers. Half the feathers were green. The other half were pink. Deep black circles were painted around her eyes, and each ear was adorned with four safety pin earrings going up in a row. An enormous black leather belt with studs and rhinestones weighed down her waist. She was wearing a glove on each hand with holes for all ten fingers to show through. The nails matched the hair.

With a look of boredom coupled with sullen contempt, she entered the room. "Yeah?" she said.

"Chastity, dear, a friend of yours is, like, here to see you."

Chastity took one long glare at the *meshulach* fidgeting uncomfortably on the cushion beneath him. Her expression spoke volumes, all of them reading: "Ain't no friend of *mine*."

UNDERMINED but undeterred, Shmuel found inspiration and encouragement in

Rule #2: Be polite. He rolled his eyes back in his best imitation of Chastity's greeting to him, and intoned sincerely, "Thank you."

Chastity's hands were on her hips. "Well?!" she snapped.

Shmuel feared to deviate from Rule #4, which demanded brevity, but he did feel that under the circumstances a little elaboration was in order.

"This, er, is not the Chastity, that is, *charity* I want, er, meant, um, *need*," Shmuel stammered. The verbal advance in no way mitigated the young woman's unfriendly disposition, but her mother immediately grasped what he was driving at.

"I dig," she said. "You're not here to see Chastity. You want my son, Wounded Knee."

Before Shmuel could formulate a response to Ginger's latest misinterpretation and clarify that what he needed was a charitable donation, she whacked the gong twice and yelled, "Knee-ee!" She then turned her attention back to her guest, making conversation to fill the gap.

"You know how Knee got his name, don't you?" she asked. Bernstein shook his head, not trusting his tongue to utter even a monosyllable.

"His father was, like, shot during a Civil Rights demonstration at Wounded Knee, South Dakota. His last great movement..." she explained, her voice cracking and a wistful tear falling from her eye, "was to save the Indians."

O N THIS NOTE Shmuel finally awoke to the fact that he was probably in the wrong house. The Last of the Mohicans wasn't exactly a likely donor for his yeshivah. The problem now was how to extricate himself from the reservation without getting an arrow between his shoulder blades.

He didn't have much time to consider his dilemma, for before long the *Kaddishel* arrived. Wounded Knee Pearlowitz was exceedingly tall, made even taller by the six-inch thatch of white mohawk bristles that ran down the center of his otherwise bald head. A rag of sorts was tied around his forehead like a sweatband and his jeans and T-shirt were ventilated with gaping holes. Unlike his sister, he was barefoot, but whereas she had shuffled zombie-like into the room, Knee came in with a flying leap, arms and legs assuming an aggressive martial-arts stance. "Hi-*ya!*" he shouted and Shmuel wondered if this was a variation on the more commonplace "Hiya, there," or if it had a more profound, esoteric meaning.

"Knee," Ginger opened with that same dazed look in her eyes, "there's someone, like, here to see you."

Knee's eyes did not roll heavenward in disgust but narrowed in suspicion. He began weaving around Shmuel in his lightfooted way, windmilling his stiffly held hands, chopping at the air and back-kicking a cushion or two. Shmuel, by now an expert at returning weird salutations, mimicked Knee's gyrations, adding a polite "Thank you."

E SCAPE WAS IMPOSSIBLE, and probably inadvisable to attempt. Shmuel decided instead to make the most of the situation. If nothing else, it was a good chance to practice his *shpiel*. He consulted his little list, which again championed brevity, but this time Shmuel made an effort to include a subject and a predicate so as to make his intentions perfectly clear.

"I go to a yeshivah in Jerusalem. It's very poor; we need money."

"Far out!" Knee responded, pulling himself up a piece of floor. "That's Donovan's bag, too. The two of you should get along real good. This is totally awesome!"

"Of course!" Ginger agreed, gonging three times before Shmuel had a chance to brace himself. "Donovan's, like, my foster son."

From behind the beaded curtain, a boy of about eighteen emerged. "Yes, Ginger?"

"Care to join us? I thought you might offer our friend a little Colombian tea!"

Shmuel's eyes dilated as wide as Lenox soup bowls. Donovan — a true flower child if ever there was one — was wearing a dress. It wasn't really a dress; it was more like a saffron-colored robe. His hair was long and silky and tied back in a ponytail with a piece of yarn. A small leather pouch dangled from his rope belt. Shmuel shook his head in disbelief as Donovan took his seat alongside him.

Ginger "formally" introduced them. "Donovan, make like an earthquake!"

Shmuel's curiosity got the better of him. "Make like an earthquake?" he echoed.

"Sure!" Ginger replied. "Make like an earthquake and SHAKE!"

DONOVAN gave him a soulful look and extended a hand. It drooped limply at his wrist. Going back to Rule #2: Be polite, Shmuel shook it. It was surprisingly smooth and smelled like the honeysuckle Shmuel knew back home in Jerusalem.

Donovan was the first to speak. "What's your sign? No, don't tell me. You must be a Libra."

"No," Shmuel said, "I'm a *meshulach*, and I'm collecting for a yeshivah..."

Ginger interrupted. "Donovan, where are your manners?"

The saffron-robed boy thumped his forehead. "Sorry, Ginger," he apologized. "It was an oversight." He dumped out what looked like Tetley's tiniest little tea leaves mixed with oregano from his leather pouch.

"No thanks," Shmuel said politely. "I'm not thirsty."

The Pearlowitzes laughed at his little joke. Earth Mother rolled the tea in small squares of paper and the whole family lit up together.

THERE WAS NO LONGER any doubt in Shmuel's mind: He was definitely in the wrong house. This family was not in any financial position to contribute anything. They didn't have enough money for furniture. They were obviously so poor they couldn't even afford dishes; they had to smoke their tea, instead of drinking it! The daughter wore her brother's hand-me-downs and had to cut her own hair, from the looks of it. One son wore torn rags and appeared to be handicapped, as evidenced by his stiff-limbed spastic movements. And the foster kid wore his *mother's* hand-me-downs. They didn't even have shoes, except for the girl, who had a pair of old boots on — in the summer, no less!

It was pathetic, and a waste of everybody's time, although the Pearlowitzes didn't seem to have anything special scheduled. Before he began the complex process of getting up off the floor, however, Shmuel furtively reached for his instruction sheet. As he perused the list, he realized that he had been faithful to each and every one of the rules and this gave him renewed confidence — especially as the sweet smoke that was wafting around the room began to have its effect on him.

Finally, his eyes focused on Rule #5: Speak their language. Shmuel unsprawled himself from his pillow. The room tilted strangely and he tried to tilt with it. As hopeless as the situation seemed, he felt it would be a mistake to omit even one of the tried-and-true directions given him by those men of vast experience. "All right," he told himself. "Give it your best shot." He cleared his throat importantly and began.

L IKE, MAN," Shmuel said, "my yeshivah in *Yerushalayim* needs bread. If they don't get some, they're going to be, you know, like, no-where! Dig?"

"We dig," the Pearlowitzes said in unison.

"That's why I'm here — to raise..."

"Our consciousness!" Donovan chimed in.

"Right *on!*" Shmuel cried emphatically, hoping that what he had said made sense.

Ginger rolled her head. "How much dough has to go?"

Shmuel tried to translate. "Dough? Dough is like bread. And bread means money!" The more the smoke filled the room, the easier it was for Shmuel to understand Ginger and Donovan. Luckily, Chastity and Wounded Knee were nap-ping — or something; he was sure their rap would be too far out for him.

"What do you say to fifty?" he asked.

"That's heavy bread, man," she answered.

"The heavier the bread, the more earning for learning," Shmuel said. Then, for good measure, he added, "Dig?"

Ginger dug. Into one of the oversized floor cushions which doubled as her handbag. The contents were soon arrayed on the Indian rug: dozens of powdered and pilled substances, a brass pipe of some sort, three or four strands of multi-colored love beads, a campaign button with the slogan "Draft Beer Not Students," followed by another that said "Nixon's Only Platform Are His Shoes," a dog-eared pamphlet entitled "Raising

Cannabis for Fun and Profit," some miscellaneous change and a few bills. At the bottom she found a checkbook.

She retrieved a pen from the thick braid on top of her head, made out a check and handed it to Shmuel. "It's been real," she said.

"Peace unto you!" Donovan added.

"*Aleichem shalom,*" Shmuel automatically responded.

Still slightly dizzy, Shmuel made his way to the door. Although he had failed in his first attempt to be a big-time collector, he took solace in the fact that he had at least provided these people with an opportunity to do a mitzvah.

A S HE APPROACHED the car, he glanced at the check. Then he glanced again, exerting himself to retain his eyeballs in their rightful sockets. He counted the zeroes a second time, then a third. Shmuel found himself hyperventilating and getting chalky in the face, only this time it wasn't from schnorrophobia. He expected the figure to change before his very eyes, but it didn't.

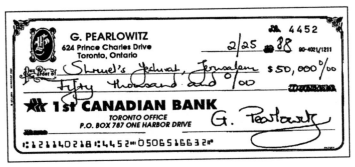

"Well, it sure took you long enough!" the driver said testily as Shmuel yanked the car door open. "A few more minutes and I would have called out the Mounties." His passenger appeared to be in a state of shock — or was it euphoria? "Well, how was it?" he asked.

Shmuel shook his head. In a voice brimming with pride and self-confidence, he replied, "Heavy, man, heavy. Totally awesome."

Heard from: Nate Kaufman (the cabbie who took Bernstein to the wrong address)

The French Have a Word for It

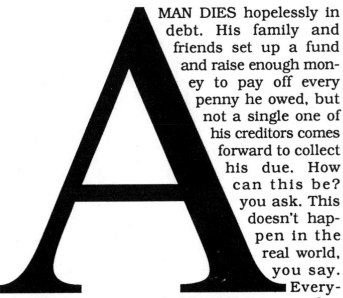

A MAN DIES hopelessly in debt. His family and friends set up a fund and raise enough money to pay off every penny he owed, but not a single one of his creditors comes forward to collect his due. How can this be? you ask. This doesn't happen in the real world, you say. Everyone demands his pound of flesh; there are no free lunches; and so on and so forth. And yet, this *did* happen.

The French have a word for it. They call it *noblesse oblige*, which literally means, "nobility obligates." *Webster's* explains it: "used to denote the obligation of honorable and generous behavior associated with high rank or birth," and *Random House Unabridged* says: "the moral obligation of those of high birth, powerful social position, etc. to act with honor, kindliness, generosity, etc."

Among Jews, the idea is a bit different. It is not our hereditary nobility which creates obligations; it is the sense of obligation that creates nobility. Wealth, social position, and high birth are of little consequence; obligations such as honor, kindliness and generosity — in short, *chessed* — are the credentials of card-carrying Jewish aristocrats.

The present account is of David Winchester, a member of this Jewish aristocracy. A man of wealth? When he died, his debts were staggering. Of high birth? Hardly. Of social position? His friends and associates were the poorest Jews in the city of Chicago. But he was a nobleman. A Jewish nobleman. One before whom the luminaries of his generation stood in awe; one who, although personally insolvent, had an unlimited line of credit among the wealthy.

Reb David Winchester was not a man whose noble birth had burdened him with obligations. On the contrary, he was a man whose sense of obligation made him an aristocrat. Like most Jewish aristocrats, Reb David would have denied that there was anything unique about himself. Those who had the privilege of making his acquaintance, however, knew better.

B ORN IN POLAND, David Winchester immi-
grated to America with his parents when
he was a small child. Even in his youth, people
noticed that there was something unusual about
him. David Winchester, it seems, was incapable
of distinguishing between theory and practice. To
be more precise, he never fully grasped the meaning of "theoretical knowledge" — everything he
learned, he applied. It was this peculiarity that
led to what was certainly the most fateful decision
of his life.

One year, as a young man of the age when
many young men today are filling out their appli-
cations to Stanford, Yale, and Ponevizh, David
spent the better part of *Tisha b'Av* absorbed in a
segment of the *Zohar* that dealt with the holiness
of the Land of Israel. That evening, as he broke his
fast, his family noted that he appeared to be
somewhat preoccupied and detached from his
surroundings. When asked if everything was all
right, the young yeshivah student was heard to
mumble something like, "I never realized..." A
month later, he was on a ship bound for *Eretz Yisrael*. David's presumption that everything he
learned was meant to be applied, was to be the
single most important factor in his personality
makeup.

For those who routinely jet back and forth to
Israel, it may be important to mention here that a
trip to the Holy Land in the 1920s, let alone an
extended stay there, was not what it is today.
Uri's Pizza and Off the Square had not yet opened.
Kleenex tissues and Coca Cola were not available, nor did Swissair and Pan Am have regular

service. On the other hand, Haj Amin al Husseini, the Grand Mufti of Jerusalem, did.

In short, why a nice Jewish boy from Chicago would want to leave home for the Chevron Yeshivah (*not* the one in Geulah and *not* the one in Givat Mordechai — the one in *Chevron*) was not something that too many people understood. For David Winchester, however, the sanctity of the Land of Israel was far more attractive than any argument to the contrary, and Chevron, with its world-renowned *mashgiach ruchani*, the famed *alter* of Slobodka, Reb Nosson Zvi Finkel and brilliant *rosh yeshivah*, Reb Moshe Mordechai Epstein, author of the *Levush Mordechai*, was an irresistible attraction.

THE CHEVRON YESHIVAH had a short and tragic history in the town from which it took its name. Founded in 1924, Chevron was a direct outgrowth of Slobodka, the famous *musar* yeshivah.

Reb Moshe Mordechai Epstein, born in 5616 (1866), grew to be one of the most revered luminaries and leaders of a generation rich in Torah scholarship. He was one of the founders of *Agudas Harabbanim* of Lithuania, and was selected in 5673 (1923) as a member of the worldwide *Mo'etzes Gedolei Hatorah* of *Agudas Yisrael* and was one of the main speakers at that year's *Kenessiah Gedolah*. Shortly thereafter, Reb Moshe Mordechai traveled to the United States as part of a delegation representing Lithuanian Jewry along with Reb Avraham Dov

Shapiro, the Kovno Rav, and Reb Avraham Yitzchak Hakohen Kook. His visit to America may have been responsible for the fact that a sizeable contingent of American *talmidim* came to study in Chevron.

Reb Moshe Mordechai Epstein had a deep love for *Eretz Yisrael* and took an active interest in contemporary settlement efforts. While still living in Lithuania, he had visited the Holy Land twice, for he believed that it was important for religious Jewry to be integrally involved in the growth of the new *yishuv*. When the Lithuanian government canceled the exemption of yeshivah students from military service, Reb Moshe Mordechai immediately began raising the money required to move the main body of the yeshivah to Chevron. He sent agents to Palestine to negotiate with the British Mandatory Government in order to secure the necessary immigration papers (*certifikatim*) for the students and *rabbanim*.

The transfer of Slobodka to *Eretz Yisrael* was a major event at the time, one that engaged not only the leaders of *Agudas Yisrael* but the president of the *Mizrachi*, Reb Meir Bar-Ilan, son of the *Netziv*, as well. The British Colonial Secretary rose in Parliament to report on the establishment of a college for the advanced study of Talmud in Chevron, and the High Commissioner for Palestine, in his report to the League of Nations, mentioned the founding of the new yeshivah in Chevron as the most important event to take place in Palestine in 1924.

With their clean-shaven faces and short coats,

the *bachurim* of Slobodka who arrived in Chevron created quite a stir in the stalwart *yishuv hayashan.* But the Chevron community, which at the time was in decline, was most pleased with the injection of new blood. So, believe it or not, were the local Arabs.

The heads of the Arab community of Chevron were welcome visitors at the home of Rabbi Epstein, and when it was rumored that the yeshivah might move elsewhere, a representation of Arab dignitaries met with the *rosh yeshivah* to detail how greatly such a move would harm the local economy. The yeshivah proved a tremendous attraction to the entire religious world, and by the fateful year of 1929, there were 265 *bachurim* enrolled, including students from the United States, England, Europe and, of course, *Eretz Yisrael.*

Arab nationalism and Jewish aspirations to establish a home in the Holy Land, however, were on a collision course, and the Chevron Yeshivah, to which young David Winchester had journeyed, found itself lodged inextricably between a rock and a hard place.

THE TINY ALLEYWAY in front of the Western Wall in Jerusalem was controlled by the *Wakf,* the Moslem equivalent of the *gizbar* of the *Beis Hamikdash,* and a number of Jewish attempts to legally transfer control had failed. Throughout the twenties, certain Jewish elements had become increasingly militant and demonstrative about their rights to pray at the Wall, which at the time was still unexcavated and a fraction of its present size. The Arabs, under the leadership of the extremist Mufti of Jerusalem — who proved to be an expert at inciting mobs into a frenzy — alleged that the Jews would try to take over the Temple Mount, where the Mosque of Omar and the Al Aksa Mosque stand, and rebuild their Holy Temple.

The Arabs were shocked when, in 1927, a teeming crowd of 20,000 Jews gathered at the Western Wall on *Tisha b'Av*, weeping and praying loudly. From that time on, friction over Jewish and Moslem holy places grew uncontrollably. Violent demonstrations and counter-demonstrations took place all during 1929, and with the High Holy Days approaching, *Eretz Yisrael* became a pressure cooker with no safety valve.

Several times during the month of August, Arab mobs forced Jewish worshipers at the Western Wall to flee. On Wednesday, the 21st of August, a Jewish child who had strayed into an Arab courtyard was stabbed, provoking more demonstrations on both sides. Two days later, on Friday, Arab mobs, incited by nationalistic sermons delivered at their Sabbath services, burst into Jewish enclaves all over Palestine and began to plunder and kill. Only the efforts of the *Haganah* and bountiful portions of Divine Providence saved Jerusalem from the tragic fate subsequently visited upon Chevron.

By this time, the entire *yishuv* had been expecting some such outbreak and, in many locales, preparations for defense had been made. Chevron was the exception that proved what the Arab masses would do if permitted. Rumors spread among the Jews of Chevron that an inflammatory letter had been circulated throughout the city, urging the Arab residents to attack their Jewish neighbors. The rumors were ignored, however, for the Jewish community members could not believe that their friends, neighbors, customers and landlords would rise up against them. Besides, in all previous disturbances, the Arabs of Chevron had remained quiescent, and the leaders of the Arab community had on numerous occasions assured the Jews that they had nothing to fear.

At one o'clock in the afternoon of that Friday, not long after Moslem Sabbath services at the local mosques had let out, a number of Arab dignitaries paid a visit to Elazar Dan Slonim, the one Jewish member of the Chevron city council, and pointed with pride to the calm maintained by the local citizenry.

Historical analysis suggests that the Chevron riots were well-planned in advance. The instigators were aware that a little well-placed disinformation in the city and surrounding villages was enough to ignite a very short fuse.

AT 2:30 P.M., a young local Arab on a motorcycle began spreading the tidings that thousands of Arabs had been killed in Jerusalem, and shortly afterward, carloads of Arabs shouting for revenge began to arrive in Chevron. Angry mobs gathered in the streets, and any Jews who happened by were set upon.

The yeshivah was the first target. Since it was Friday afternoon the building was empty, save for two souls. One was the Yemenite *shamash*, who managed to escape and hide in a cistern. The other was Shmuel Rosenholtz, known around the yeshivah simply as the *masmid*. Though it was still early afternoon, Shmuel had already changed into his Shabbos clothing and returned to the *beis midrash* to resume learning.

Rosenholtz was so absorbed in his studies that he did not even look up when the crazed crowd burst in. A rock struck him in the head and blood poured over his *Gemara*. Half senseless, he somehow struggled to his feet and made his way to the door where the mob set upon him with knives and axes, turning his body into a sieve.

Towards nightfall the disturbances died down. The British authorities had ample time to prepare for dealing with a possible resumption of rioting the next day, but they did nothing of the sort. The Jews were instructed to merely stay in their homes and assured that if they did, they would be safe.

The next morning, the city again filled rapidly with Arabs from the outlying villages, who, together with the locals, rampaged through the streets, destroying Jewish lives and property. Rocks, clubs, knives and axes were the weapons of choice, and victim after victim succumbed to multiple stab wounds. Eyewitnesses told of horribly mutilated bodies.

The entire event took but two hours. In all, sixty-seven Jews — men, women and children —

were killed. Fifty-nine were buried the next night in five communal graves; eight more died later of their wounds. The date of the massacre: August 24, 1929, the eighteenth of Av, *Tarpat*.

The 500 or so Jews who had survived were eager to leave, and by Tuesday night all, except the one Jewish member of the police force, had been evacuated to Jerusalem. The planners of the 1929 Chevron massacre had achieved their aim. The holy city of Chevron which, with the exception of the Crusader period, had known continuous Jewish settlement from the time of Yehoshua, was now *Judenrein*.

Among the evacuees was Reb Moshe Mordechai Epstein. He had lost twenty-four of his boys, and it was said that he never recovered from the tragedy. He returned his soul to his Father in Heaven five years later, his last years marked by frailty and suffering.

D AVID WINCHESTER was also a victim of the Chevron Massacre. Another "human sieve," he was stabbed thirteen times. In later years, this gentlest of souls related how he first came to understand the commandment to obliterate the nation of Amalek, including women and children, while he lay on the floor bleeding and playing dead. With one eye just barely open he had watched — horror-stricken — as the Arab children of Chevron approached motionless bodies and kicked them. A groan would prove fatal, as they directed the murderers to return and finish the job.

David Winchester returned to Chicago more dead than alive. Since he had survived, he was committed to fulfilling the vow he had made on the blood-drenched floor: that he would devote the rest of his life to *chessed.*

REB DAVID WINCHESTER assumed a pulpit in Albany Park, Chicago's poorest Jewish community and the one most suited for Rabbi Winchester. The poor, weak, sickly and downtrodden gravitated to the spiritual leader who sought them out. On any given night one could behold several homeless Jews sleeping on benches in the synagogue, and the rabbi tending to their needs, bringing food from his own kitchen.

The cold of Chicago's winters is legendary, and an acquaintance recalls spotting a coatless Rabbi Winchester walking home on a bone-chilling night. When asked what had happened, Reb David's answer was evasive, but it didn't take too much research to discover that he had given "the coat off his back" to one of his *shul*'s "guests."

Reb David Winchester's generosity soon became well-known. His friends found his total disregard for *olam hazeh* astonishing, and at times they even took measures to protect him from himself. The *Gemara* tells of a righteous Jew who gave so much money to charity that the *gabba'im* would hide when they saw him in the marketplace, for fear that he would compel them to accept his last *dinar*. Such a man was Reb David. During the entire period that David Winchester gave *shiurim* at the Chicago yeshivah, the *hanhalah* had his paycheck delivered directly to his wife, lest their rabbi cash it and give it all away before reaching home.

His generosity resulted in a life endured on the brink of bankruptcy. Nevertheless, whenever there was a mitzvah to be done, money seemed to be no problem. On one occasion, he heard that the local B'nai Brith chapter was planning to have a function at which non-kosher food would be served. Upon inquiry, Reb Winchester was politely informed that kosher catering was simply too expensive. The next day he appeared with a check to cover the higher cost of kosher food.

ONE who despises gifts will live," the Book of Proverbs teaches. David Winchester had no problem with gifts; he simply refused them. To those who wished to shower him with presents he suggested instead that they extend him a personal loan, which he immediately donated to some worthy cause or other. Accordingly, Reb David never managed to get out from under a heavy burden of debt, but those who knew him eventually became wise to his ways, and as a result, his credit never ran out.

On one occasion, Reb David visited an indigent man in the hospital and found that the poor fellow was deeply depressed. It seems that the patient realized that he was very near death and knew he had no money to pay for a cemetery plot, casket or headstone. Rabbi Winchester tried to assure him that he would see to everything, but the man remained inconsolable.

Reb David tried to discover what else was troubling the man, and finally got him to confide that his conscience would not allow him to take advantage of the rabbi, whom everyone in Chicago knew to be a poor man himself. Nothing Reb David could say would reassure the man until Winchester sped off to the office of Paul Rosenberg, one of his regular contributors. There he prevailed upon his benefactor to come to the hospital and promise the dying man that he, and not Rabbi Winchester, would cover the burial expenses.

Whenever generous people in Chicago wanted to extend a hand to the needy, they were in for a surprise: it was as though someone had been there previously and scribbled "Winchester was here." Once, when the young Rabbi Aryeh Rottman offered to help an aging woman carry her bags home, he was startled to find that she lived in a filthy one-room hovel beneath the stairs of the subway. Looking around, he could think of nothing to say but, "You ought to be in touch with David Winchester."

"Ahh, Rabbi Winchester," the woman said, her face brightening. "He's the one who paid for my operation! What a wonderful man. He visits me here all the time." But "visiting" the poor is a pale description of the activities of David Winchester, who would sometimes simply disappear from home for several days to help nurse a poor person back to health.

R EB MOSHE MORDECHAI Epstein would vehemently dispute the contention that David Winchester's career of *chessed* commenced only after the massacre. As a matter of course he always rose in deference when Winchester, then a young unassuming *bachur* clad in American-style clothing, entered the room. Pressed for the reason he had adopted this custom, Reb Moshe Mordechai related a chilling story:

A few years before the 1929 riots, two students of the Chevron Yeshivah contracted a highly contagious, fatal disease. Obviously the boys had to be kept under quarantine, and no one was allowed to have any physical contact with them. Accordingly, they were isolated in a small building near the yeshivah, and their meals were provided on trays deposited in a shack that stood midway between the yeshivah and the boys' quarters.

As the disease progressed, the boys grew weaker and weaker until they could no longer even crawl out of their room to the half-way house. All of the members of the yeshivah felt terrible for them, and many wanted to be *mevaker cholim*, but they were deathly afraid to approach the quarantined area.

Reb Moshe Mordechai, however, realized that even such a legitimate fear could not absolve the *rosh yeshivah* from visiting and caring for his students. After significant preparation for the fateful visit, he made his way to their quarters, his pace marked by trepidation. There, to his astonishment, he found David Winchester, tenderly waiting on the dying lads and actually placing the food into their mouths, for they were too weak by that time to feed themselves.

Little wonder then that when David Winchester departed for a better world than this one, his funeral was well-attended. At the time of his passing, just as during his rich lifetime, he was, as usual, abysmally in debt. The many who came to honor him were not surprised when they heard one of the strangest announcements ever made at a *levayah*. "The friends of David Winchester have raised the necessary funds to cover any and all of the great *tzaddik*'s outstanding obligations. Anyone who is owed money should contact Mr.____."

In the coming months, not a single individual came forward... No doubt they felt they had been adequately recompensed by the mere privilege of having known Reb David, a man who was the embodiment of *noblesse oblige.*

Heard from: Rabbi Aryeh Rottman and Dov Zupnick

Caution: Jewish Minds at Work

THERE is a propensity of certain intellectuals to support oppressive regimes, evil doctrines, and perfidious beliefs, and later claim that they were misled. As one honest (and witty) intellectual wrote, "It is no defense whatever for an intellectual to say that he was duped, since that is what, as an intellectual, he should never allow to happen to him."

Jewish "intellectuals" throughout modern history have been innocent of neither the misplaced support nor the untenable rationalization, and therefore have not earned our unqualified esteem.

But there have always been those true Jewish intellectuals worthy of our appreciation and even emulation: those Jews who combined their God-given intellect with wit and resourcefulness to overcome adversaries, serve the Lord, and help mankind. Below are three examples, some better known than others, of the proverbial *Yiddishe kop* — the Jewish mind at work.

DON AGUILAR was the conductor of the Royal Orchestra in Barcelona during the time of the Spanish Inquisition. Like many of his fellow Jews, Don Aguilar only pretended to have converted to Christianity in order to avoid the mandatory death sentence, but in secret he continued to follow the faith of his forefathers. The Marranos, as these clandestine Jews were known, lived in constant danger and at perpetual risk of discovery. Determined to observe the precepts of Judaism despite their precarious circumstances, they became exceedingly adept at finding the means to do so without arousing suspicion.

Don Aguilar longed to hear the blasts of the *shofar* on Rosh Hashanah, one of the many Jewish rituals that were impossible to perform secretly. He contemplated this problem for some time before he came upon the solution.

On the Holy Day itself, Don Aquilar presented a concert that featured music from different lands played on unusual "ethnic" instruments.

As leading Church and government officials watched, listened and applauded appreciatively at the strange blasts that issued from the ram's horn, they never suspected that they were in fact witnessing the mitzvah of the *shofar* being performed in accord with the precepts of Jewish law.

ONE OF the most famous "*Yiddishe kep*" of all time belonged to the legendary Hershel Ostropolier, town wit, beadle of the local *shtieble*, and occasional wagon driver for Reb Baruch, the *tzaddik* of Mezebusz. Reb Baruch was once traveling from Minsk to Dvinsk, when he noticed that something was on his driver's mind. "Hershel, what are you thinking about?" Reb Baruch inquired. "It's obvious that you want to ask me something."

"Yes, Rebbe, but, er, it's a personal question, and..."

"Now, now, Hershel," Reb Baruch assured him. "You needn't hesitate. Ask away."

"Well, I've been wondering... What does it feel like to be a Rebbe?"

Reb Baruch smiled. "Hmmm. That's a difficult question to answer. But I have an idea: Why don't we exchange clothes — I'll pretend to be the *baal agalah* [wagon driver], and you will be the Rebbe. Then you'll see for yourself how it feels!"

"With pleasure!" Hershel cried excitedly. Not only did the two switch clothes, they also switched roles. Hershel instantly became the illustrious passenger, sitting erect and gazing out at the passing scenery. And Reb Baruch, now dressed as Hershel Ostropolier, took up his part in this innocent charade by hunching over the reins of the horse as he guided the coach into the shtetl. When the villagers discovered who their guest was, they crowded around the carriage, begging for blessings.

"Rebbe, please bless me with *parnasah*!"

"Rebbe, I need a *shidduch* for my daughter!"

"Rebbe, please bless me with good health!"

Unfazed, Hershel, seated in the rear of the coach, proceeded to generously dispense one blessing after another. "You should be wealthier than the Czar's cook!" he cried out to one. "Your daughter should find as fine a mate as your wife did!" he called out to another. "*Zie gezunt!*" he told a third.

EVERYTHING WAS GOING WELL and Hershel was feeling not only magnanimous but exceedingly self-confident — until the local Gentile *porutz* stepped forward. For years, he had been trying to find a way to get more work out of his Jewish farm workers, but they had insisted that their religion forbade them to labor on the Sabbath. It infuriated him that he had to pay Gentile peasants out of his own pocket so that his herds would get milked and his farm equipment wouldn't lie idle on the seventh day of every week. No threats or torments he could devise, no penalties he would demand, no rewards he might offer, had succeeded in convincing the Jews to comply.

Wise enough to know not to turn to the authorities for such matters — for who knew what *that* might cost him — the landowner had begun to explore another avenue. He had started studying the Bible, with the intention of finding in it a way to prove to the Jews that the religion they espoused was nonsensical. Then, he was sure, they would realize the folly of their strict adherence to it and he would at last get a full week's worth of work out of them.

The only problem was that the more he studied, the more sense the Jewish faith made, even to him, a devout Christian. However, he persevered, and at last, after rereading and reexamining the text, he found just what he had been seeking. And now, with this great scholar's visit to the village, he had a golden opportunity to present his case in a way that would publicly humiliate them all. His satisfaction would be two-fold: he would convince the Jews to forfeit their day of rest and also get back at them for their years of indolence and the financial losses he'd incurred.

The *porutz* approached "Reb Baruch" and in a loud, resounding voice challenged: "It is said that you are not only a pious, righteous Jew, but an outstanding scholar as well. If that is so, then surely you know that your religious laws have no foundation whatsoever."

A gasp rose from the crowd of villagers, but no one dared to restrain their wealthy landowner. Everyone's livelihood depended upon him.

The *porutz* went on. "You Jews maintain that your Bible contains all the laws that govern your lives, including the commandment to rest on the seventh day. I maintain that that law is as baseless as the one concerning eating dairy and meat products together. Why do I say this law is baseless? Because your own patriarchs did not observe it! In your own Bible it is clearly stated that Abraham served his guests meat and milk."

The villagers were simple folk and none of them knew how to reply to the landowner, but even if they had known what to say, none had the audacity to say it. As one, they turned their heads toward "Reb Baruch," praying that his sagacious response would refute the landowner's claims.

Hershel Ostropolier began to perspire under his rabbinic raiments. His heart pounded in his chest and the *shtreimel* on his head suddenly seemed to weigh a ton. He knew he was in deep trouble.

Hershel was the same man who once had gone into a *shul*, stacked up a wall of *sefarim* four feet high, and then had taken a nap behind them. Now he was being asked to explain a most difficult passage in the Torah, and the answer he produced would affect the lives of every one of the poor villagers before him.

H E CONSIDERED his options: If he answered incorrectly, he would embarrass the Torah and the One Who had given it. If he didn't answer at all, he would embarrass his Rebbe. And if he admitted to having exchanged places with the real Reb Baruch, he would end up embarrassing himself!

"Reb Baruch" stroked his beard, and thought and thought. Finally, it came to him. He looked the *porutz* squarely in the eye and declared, "Why, this matter is so simple that even my unlettered wagon driver would have no trouble answering it!"

B EREL KASACHKOFF, like thousands of his brethren at the time of the Russian Revolution, knew that freedom to live as a Jew *and* as a human being mandated escaping from the Soviet Union. The Russians knew this as well and accordingly stationed sentries all along their borders.

A problem, Berel conceded, but nothing a *Yiddishe kop* could not overcome. One might say this was a rather flippant attitude, considering that the border guards were heavily armed and instructed to shoot on sight. Berel, however, had big plans and was not about to let a technicality — no matter how formidable — stand in his way. Thus, armed with only his wit and a prayer on his lips, Berel headed for the Polish frontier.

When Berel arrived at the most secluded spot he could find close to the border, he discovered that even there the border crossing was heavily guarded, and he was forced to scuttle his first plan. As he considered his options, he noticed that not only was the area well-patrolled, but the sentries were in a state of high alert.

It was only four months since the Revolution had erupted and whereas every citizen feared his own neighbor, Red Army soldiers were afraid of their own shadow. Not an especially auspicious climate for breaking the law...until Berel concocted a way to use it to his advantage.

BRAVELY AND DEFIANTLY he made a beeline for the guard house and marched off toward his destiny. He strode right past the few merchants lined up at the border crossing, each of them displaying their papers and travel permits. Berel did not have a legitimate document to his name. The only identification papers he possessed had been forged to enable him to avoid the draft; an amateurish job, but the best he had been able to afford, it was the last thing he would present to guards who had instructions to refer all questions directly to jail.

"Halt!" ordered one of the soldiers.

Berel kept marching.

"I said, 'HALT!'"

Berel kept right on marching.

A second soldier aimed his rifle at Berel's heart. Berel could hear the cartridge slide into the breech.

Berel continued marching toward Poland, on a collision course with the soldiers and their itchy trigger fingers.

"Papers!" the guard commanded.

Berel looked at him unbelievingly. "What did you say?" he asked.

"Papers! Let me see your identification papers!"

"My papers? You want to see MY papers? You mean you're asking to see MY PAPERS? Why, I should have all of you shot! Don't you know who I am?"

FOR A MOMENT there was silence. Berel's eyes blazed with anger, fury, wrath and righteous indignation. By this time, he was fairly shouting. "WELL?" he bellowed. "DO YOU KNOW WHO I AM?"

The soldiers looked at each other. Before they could answer, Berel snarled, "Let me see *your* papers!" and then screamed "NOW!"

Stunned by the ferocity of his voice and the authority of his manner, the soldiers began fumbling through their pockets.

Berel continued shouting. "I ought to have you shot, then drawn and quartered for good measure. The absolute insolence! The ultimate impudence! The outrageous audacity! And you call yourselves soldiers?!"

"We didn't know—"

"SILENCE!" Berel ordered. The guards meekly passed him their papers. He gave them a quick inspection, then threw them on the ground. "Fools! Idiots! You can be sure that when I return from my official mission I will have your HEADS!" he roared. Then Berel spat in disgust at their feet, and proceeded to cross the Russian checkpoint into freedom.

As he entered Poland, he couldn't resist a parting shot. When he estimated that he was beyond the range of their rifles, he shouted at the top of his lungs, "*NOW* DO YOU KNOW WHO I AM?"

"N-n-no," they shouted back.

"Berel Kasachkoff, at your service!" He tipped his hat, gave the stunned guardsmen a brief but polite bow, and then ran for his life.

Heard from: Chana Poupko

❧
Glossary

Glossary

The following glossary provides a partial explanation of some of the foreign words and phrases used in this book. The spelling, tense and definitions reflect the way the specific term is used in "*Hey, Taxi!*" Often, there are alternate spellings and meanings. Foreign words and phrases translated in the text are not included in this section.

ACHARONIM: Talmudic scholars of the last five hundred years.

AGUNAH: lit., a "chained woman"; a woman whose marriage has been terminated *de facto* but not *de jure*, and who is therefore forbidden to remarry because she is still technically married to her absent husband.

ALEICHEM SHALOM: "May peace be upon you"; usual response to the greeting "*Shalom aleichem,*" which means the same thing.

ALIYAH L'REGEL: holiday pilgrimage to the holy city of Jerusalem.

ALTE BOCHUR: (Yid., colloq.) lit., old boy; an elderly bachelor.

ALTER: (Yid.) aged one; a title of respect.

ARNONA: municipal taxes.

ASHKENAZIM: Jews of European ancestry.

AV BEIS DIN: lit., father of the court; chief Rabbinical judge in a BEIS DIN.

BAAL TESHUVAH: penitent who has returned to religious observance.

BAALEI TZEDAKAH: philanthropists.

BACHUR, BACHURIM: unmarried yeshivah student(s).

BALABUSTA: (Yid., colloq.) efficient, capable homemaker.

BARUCH HASHEM: lit., the Lord is blessed; thank God.

BEIN HAZMANIM: lit., between times or semesters; yeshivah intersession.

BEIS DIN: court of Jewish law.

BEIS HAMIKDASH: the Holy Temple.

BEIS MIDRASH: a house of study used for both Torah study and prayer.

BEZEK: Israel's telephone company.

BO'I: (f.) "Come here."

BUBBE: (Yid.) grandmother.

B'SEDER: okay.

CHAREDIM: devoutly religious Jews.

CHASSID, CHASSIDIM: devout follower(s) of a REBBE.

CHASSUNAH: (Yid.) a wedding.

CHESSED: acts of lovingkindness.

CHOLENT: (Yid.) a traditional stew prepared on Friday afternoon and kept hot until the midday Shabbos meal.

DAVENED: (Yid.) prayed.

DAYYAN, DAYYANIM: Rabbinical court judge(s).

DERECH ERETZ: respect.

DIN: a dispute judged by a Rabbinical court.

DIVREI TORAH: usually brief expositions on Torah subjects.

ERETZ YISRAEL: the Land of Israel.

EREV: eve.

GABBA'IM: wardens of the synagogue who collect and dispense charity.

GELT: (Yid.) money.

GEMACH, GEMACHIM: contraction of *gemilus chassadim*, performing acts of kindness; interest-free loan or other benevolent funds.

GEMARA: 1. commentary on the Mishnah (together they comprise the Talmud); 2. a volume of the Talmud.

GET: a writ of divorce.

GEULAH: final Redemption.

GEVALD: (Yid.) "Oh my!"

GEZUNT: (Yid.) health.

GIZBAR: treasurer; collector.

GLEZL: (Yid.) a small glass.

GOYIM: lit., nations; Gentiles.

GVIR: a man of substance.

HAGANAH: clandestine Jewish defense forces prior to the establishment of the State of Israel.

HAKADOSH BARUCH HU: the Holy One, blessed be He.

HAKAFOS: seven circuits made by the worshipers bearing Torah scrolls on SIMCHAS TORAH.

HAKOL B'SEDER: "Everything is all right."

HALACHAH: Jewish law.

HANHALAH: administration.

KADDISHEL: (Yid., colloq.) the boy who will say the *kaddish* prayer of mourning for his parents upon their demise.

KENESSIAH GEDOLAH: the grand assembly of great Rabbis.

KIDDISH: spread of delicacies served after Shabbos services.

KISHKES: (Yid.) innards.

KLAL YISRAEL: the community of Israel; all Jewry.

KOL HAKAVOD: "Congratulations!"

KOLLEL: post-graduate yeshivah comprised of young married students who receive monthly stipends.

KOP, KEP: (Yid.) head(s).

KRECHTZ: (Yid.) groan.

KRENK: (Yid.) sick.

KVELLED: (Yid.) beamed with pride.

LANTSMAN: (Yid.) one who hails from the same village or country.

LASHON HARA: slander; gossip; a derogatory or damaging statement about someone.

LEVAYAH: funeral.

MADRICHAH: (f.) a counselor.

MAMA LOSHEN: (Yid.) mother tongue.

MASHGIACH RUCHANI: the dean of students in a yeshivah who acts as a spiritual guide and adviser.

MASHIACH: the Messiah.

MASMID: a diligent student.

MAZAL TOV: lit., good fortune; "Very hearty congratulations!"

MENORAH: candelabra lit on Chanukah.

MESHUGAAS: (Yid.) weirdness.

MESHULACH, MESHULACHIM: lit., messenger(s); itinerant fund-raiser(s) for a charitable organization or institution.

MEVAKER CHOLIM: visiting the infirm.

MEZUZAH: parchment scroll with selected Torah verses placed in a container and affixed to gates and doorposts of Jewish homes.

MIDDAH K'NEGED MIDDAH: measure for measure.

MINYAN, MINYANIM: quorum of ten adult Jewish males; the basic unit of community for certain religious purposes, including prayer.

MISNAGDIM: individuals who opposed the Chassidic movement.

MITZVOS: lit., commandments; good deeds.

MIZRACHI: the Religious Zionist Movement.

MOSHAV: a cooperative agricultural settlement similar to a kibbutz.

MUSSAR: 1. school of thought emphasizing ethical perfection; 2. moral teachings; 3. a lecture on ethics.

NEBACH: (Yid.) unfortunate.

NU, SAVTA'LE, MAH AHT OMERET: "Well, Grandma, what do you say?"

OLAM HAZEH: lit., this world; earthly existence.

ORACH CHAIM: section of the SHULCHAN ARUCH which deals with daily life.

PARNASAH: livelihood.

PAROCHES: curtain of the ark in a synagogue which contains the Torah scrolls.

PARSHIOS: Torah portions; parchments.

PAZGAZ: Israeli gas company.

PORUTZ: (Yid.) a wealthy landowner.

PROTEKTZIA: influence; connections.

PUSHKA: (Yid.) a charity box.

RABBANIM: Rabbis.

REBBE: 1. Rabbi; usually a Talmud teacher; 2. instructor; 3. Chassidic leader.

RISHONIM: lit., first ones; European scholars of the eleventh through fifteenth centuries.

ROSH YESHIVAH, ROSHEI YESHIVAH: yeshivah dean(s).

SAVTA, SAVTA'LE: grandmother, grandma.

SCHNORRER: (Yid.) a freeloader; a fund solicitor.

SEFER, SEFARIM: book(s) of religious content.

SEFER TORAH, SIFREI TORAH: Torah scroll(s).

SEPHARDIM: Jews of Mediterranean or North African ancestry.

SHABBOS KALLAH: an informal get-together of a bride and her friends on the Shabbos preceding her wedding.

SHADCHAN: a matchmaker.

SHALIACH: an emissary.

SHAMASH: a synagogue caretaker; the Rabbi's assistant.

SHEIGETZ: a non-Jew.

SHEITEL: (Yid.) a wig worn by a married woman.

SHEMA YISRAEL: prayer (recited daily) proclaiming the oneness of God and affirming faith in Him and His Torah.

SHEMIRAS HALASHON: guarding one's speech to avoid slander and defamation, in accord with the Torah's precepts.

SHERUT: a shuttle taxi.

SHIDDUCH: a (matrimonial) match.

SHIUR (SHIURIM): Torah lecture(s).

SHLEPPED: (Yid.) dragged; hauled.

SHMATTES: (Yid.) rags.

SHMUESS: (Yid). a MUSSAR discourse.

SHOFAR: a ram's horn, blown especially on Rosh Hashanah and the end of Yom Kippur.

SHOMER YISRAEL: lit., Guardian of Israel; scriptural verse which relates how God watches over the Jewish people.

SHOMROT: guardians.

SHPIEL: (Yid.) an amusing play.

SHTENDERS: (Yid.) lecterns, used in place of desks in many yeshivas.

SHTICK: (Yid.) gimmicks and pranks.

SHTIEBEL: (Yid.) a small, informal, intimate room for prayer or study.

SHTREIMEL: an ornamental, fur-trimmed hat worn by CHAASSIDIM on Shabbos and festivals.

SHUL: (Yid.) a synagogue.

SHVITZIN: (Yid.) sweating.

SIDDUR: a prayer book.

SIMCHAH: lit. joy; a celebration.

SIMCHAS TORAH: the holiday of the rejoicing of the Torah; the festival concluding Sukkos.

S'TOME: "Silence!"

TALLIS: a four-cornered, fringed prayer shawl.

TALMID, TALMIDIM: student(s).

TANTE: (Yid.) aunt.

TAPUACH: apple.

TARPAT: the Hebrew acronym for the date on the Jewish calendar corresponding to 1929.

TEFILLIN: black leather boxes containing verses from the Torah which are bound to the arm and head of a man during morning prayers.

TEHILLIM: psalms; the Book of Psalms.

TISHA B'AV: the ninth day of the month of Av; the fast day commemorating the destruction of the First and Second Temples.

TODAH RABBAH: "Thank you very much."

TZADDIK: a righteous person.

TZAROS: (TZURIS —Yid.) troubles.

TZAV HACHAIM: a living will.

TZAVA'AH: a will.

TZEDAKAH: charity.

TZEIDAH LADERECH: provisions for a journey.

TZNIUS: modesty.

VASSER: (Yid.) water.

YAMIM NORAIM: lit., days of awe; the ten days of penitence from Rosh Hashanah through Yom Kippur.

YERUSHALAYIM: Jerusalem.

YESHIVISH: (Yid., colloq.) similar to mannerisms common among yeshivah students.

YIDDISHE KOP, KEP: (Yid.) Jewish intellect.

YISHUV (HAYASHAN): lit., settlement; the early settlement of Jews in ERETZ YISRAEL.

YISRAEL: Israel.

YOM HAATZMAUT: Israel's Independence Day.

YOM HADIN: lit., day of judgment; Rosh Hashanah, the Jewish New Year.

YORED, YORDIM: emigrant(s) from Israel.

YUNTIFDIKKA: (Yid., colloq.) festive; appropriate for a Yom Tov, or holiday.

ZECHUS, ZECHUYOS: merit(s).

ZHID, ZHIDIN: Russian pejorative for Jew.

ZIE GEZUNT: (Yid.) "Be well!"

ZOHAR: holy kabbalistic text.

ZT"L: Hebrew acronyn of "May the memory of the TZADDIK be a blesing."